THE AGE OF GUISE

First paperback edition October 2021

Book design by Natalia Junqueira

Editing by Mike Valentino and Alisha Hammel

ISBN 978-1-7379565-0-1 (paperback)

ISBN 978-1-7379565-1-8 (ebook)

ISBN 978-1-7379565-2-5 (audiobook)

ISBN 978-1-7379565-3-2 (hardcover)

Library of congress control number 1-10872844421

The price of hating other human beings is loving oneself less...
You don't have to teach people to be human.
You have to teach them how to stop being inhuman.

ELDRIDGE CLEAVER

CONTENTS

THE AGE OF GUISE

The first few days after Kenny's suicide were the worst. After the initial shock, dark days of grief settled in among my small family and crew. What followed were the agonizing questions of why, and what happened?

Examining these questions was like sliding down the sharp edge of a razor blade, only to climb back up and slide down its salty dull side. No answers were found, the quest only bringing us agonizingly back to the grief. Within this piercing and searing loop is where I will yank off the warm covers and illuminate the cold facts.

My conjecture was that he never got over his mother abandoning him at such an early age. Maybe, maybe not; nevertheless, the fact remains that my nineteen year old cousin Ken Conrad Guise is dead and gone.

Kenny was the only son of my mother's only brother, which made him my first cousin. I never met Kenny's mother, relying only upon first hand testimony from my parents to try and understand what sort of person she was. Helen was a conservative white woman from Michigan's Upper Peninsula. Over the years my mom described her in a few different ways; German-Irish, well educated, and plain looking. According to my father, she was plump, pale and the shape of her face reminded him of a six foot tall Sir Winston Churchill. He went on to say that she was a bit fast in the ass, or loose in the ass, I can't remember his exact words. I also don't know if this was true or not, but her grandmother did own a bordello, though they always tactfully referred to it as a motel.

My parents did agree that she was pale complected with shoulder length red hair with a neat part over her left temple. She was covered in tan freckles, too numerous to count on her cheeks, arms and oddly enough also on her wrists. Her most prominent facial features were her pointy nose and bushy eyebrows, both of which she kept covered with white powder.

At 26 years old Helen was exactly the same size that she was in college which was a solid size 16. Her daily wardrobe also hadn't changed much, consisting of knee length madras and tartan plaid skirts which accentuated her curvy hips, and long sleeved collared blouses, in white and on occasion blue which accentuated her pendulous and full breasts. Footwear was always her scuffed up brown penny loafers unless she was in church, in which case she wore square heel black wedges size 15 extra wide.

Helen was overly fond of blue eye shadow, which appeared green from time to time, around her pale blue eyes. This led my father to question the health of her gall bladder which she insisted was working just fine. She was seldom seen without foundation smeared across her forehead and chin. My parents both privately referred to Helen as, "Lady Maybelline."

Uncle Ivan, Kenny's father, wasn't her first choice in men, but she liked how he seemed to worship her which was something she didn't find in white men, who tended to prefer smaller women. She had been taught by her family early on to stay away from black, brown and yellow men. Her father had informed her that any race other than the white race was substandard, and beneath her station.

She strictly adhered to this rule throughout her years at the University of Michigan. Once she graduated she discovered that the men she dated didn't care about her education or how smart she was, they simply wanted sex from her. She discovered that giving men orgasms helped their health and even their memory, because afterwards they all seemed to remember they had an early morning meeting, class, or taxes to file and needed to immediately leave.

Helen's parents split up the year that she graduated from college, which offered some evidence of her mindset back then. She and her mom were stunned when her father ran off with their cleaning lady, a brown beauty from the Dominican Republic, and left the family high and dry. He was never seen or heard from again.

This event was so overwhelming to Helen that instead of joining the work force after college, she volunteered to serve with the Baptist Women's Aid Society. Due to her youthful exuberance they put Helen to work in the field as a missionary.

It was on one of her missionary assignments to a migrant workers camp in Columbiana, Ohio where she met my uncle, The Right Reverend Ivan Conrad Guise who at the time was brand new to the ministry.

After they met she stuck to her game plan, which was no sex for the first two dates, and after that only her skillful fellatio would be utilized, which essentially made her a virgin bride. What she found endearing was that my uncle appreciated her intelligence, unlike the other men she had tried to rope into a relationship. He seemed to be in possession of a good memory, too, because after the orgasm, my uncle had no other place to be except with her.

However, the twists and turbulences within their brief marriage began almost immediately. Uncle Ivan was known by all of us in the family to prefer men to women for as long as anyone could remember. I can only imagine how shocked everyone was, when he got married. In 1957, they were the first so-called inter-racial couple in our town.

They had no place to live in the months after their marriage, so my parents let them live in our house. There was a large spare room, with its own bathroom and shower, which they lived in for 18 months.

My father told me there was something very different about them, which caught his attention. He said my uncle did all the cooking for the family, and he enjoyed that, but not as much as my mom. The fact was that Helen couldn't cook. If she did cook, some of her food combinations were culturally off putting to the family. She boiled hot dogs and served them with potato chips on folded white bread and called that a meal. When she eventually learned to make potato salad she put raisins in it, which made it look like writhing German roaches had infested it. This caused my father to have a flashback from his time during World War II in Europe, and he couldn't eat at all that night.

Other abhorrent and repugnant concoctions included steamed rice with blueberries, scrambled eggs with raisins, macaroni and cheese with green peas, and the last straw was her mashed potatoes. After boiling twenty spuds, she mashed them with salt, butter and milk, then for some reason she added a banana! My stomach turns just recalling it. This made my father so sick that he missed two days of work. After this they tried their best to keep her out of the kitchen.

My uncle also couldn't open jars, and after a while he stopped trying and opening jars became Helen's job. She also took out the garbage, shoveled snow, mowed the lawn and helped my father with repairs. In other words, in the 1950s Aunt Helen did all the traditional male jobs and my uncle spent his time polishing his nails, cutting out recipes in magazines, and practicing his singing.

My father recalled that most mornings Helen wore men's blue bedroom slippers to the kitchen table, and noted that she looked as if she were standing on a diving board, because her toes protruded beyond the edge of the slippers. Mom said she'd send Helen back to her room most mornings, because her breasts were spilling out of her robe while they were at the breakfast table, which distracted my father from reading the morning newspaper.

My parents at that time hosted cocktail parties once a month for their friends, many of whom were Buppies -Black Urban Professionals - accountants, business owners, doctors and a retired judge.

One party in particular stood out in my mother's memory. Everyone was having a nice time, when Helen got tipsy and began explaining how she had never seen a black doctor before. She went on to say that he must be a veterinarian since he wouldn't ever be allowed to treat human beings. When my uncle attempted to intervene she loudly accused him of "not screwing me in three months!"

One bright Sunday morning, my mother was up before the sun and went into her kitchen to make coffee. She screamed and became light headed when she discovered Helen washing a pair of her bloody cotton underwear in her kitchen sink. She went about trying to explain how this was no place to be washing her underwear, while she proceeded to bleach down the entire kitchen.

Not long after these events, Helen commenced to making sexual overtures toward my father. My mother began to find long red hairs in many unexplainable places, the refrigerator, and even in her shower. The proverbial last straw occurred only after she found strings of red hair in my father's underwear.

Right after that, she found an apartment for her brother and new wife. Less than ten months later Kenny was born.

A year after Kenny was born, two significant things happened; I was born and Helen took Kenny to visit her mom in Michigan, and never returned.

If I can say one good thing about Helen and her mother, at least they shipped Kenny to my parents and his father every summer without fail.

LAKE MICHIGAN

Throughout our childhood Kenny and I were like brothers and best friends. Though he was older, and could run faster, throw farther, jump higher and was an all-around natural athlete, the love of sports didn't dominate his time. Kenny instead preferred to spend his days reading. He would read books on Geography, Mechanics, and Ecology in between monthly issues of Sports Illustrated magazine. He didn't just look at the pictures in Sports Illustrated like I did, he scoured the magazine from cover to cover like a sponge.

Kenny at 15 years old was tall and lean. His smooth light brown skin stretched tightly over a masculine well-proportioned face. His light brown eyes were hypnotizing bright orbs above his high cheekbones. He kept his straight brown hair brushed down on the sides and brushed forward on the top, with a messy part high on the left temple.

The local girls would all stare at him, and go out of their way to speak to him. In fact, even some adult women would slow down and affectionately cat call, if we were walking or riding our bikes. He had those sort of multiracial good looks, and an amazing physique, that made people stop and stare.

While many knew Kenny as brutally handsome, I knew him as an incredibly smart and sensitive person.

Kenny was kind to me, and protective. I like to say he was one of my first teachers, like an older brother taking the time to explain about girls, sex, and even politics all of which at the time I knew absolutely nothing about.

One of his favorite subjects was Lake Michigan which he spoke to me about incessantly, mostly facts and figures, of how many shipwrecks there were, how big it was, and of its shore-line beauty.

He spoke a great deal of the bald Cypress, White Maple, and Birch trees that grew near the cabin his granny owned. The times he spent there in the fall, before the first snow, he described as happy times. Of all the things he loved and spoke of, a particular Cypress tree seemed etched in his memory. This mighty tree he explained was at least 170 feet tall and stood proudly near the cabin, right on Lake Michigan.

He told of a rope tied to a thick low branch where he could swing and then leap off and plunge into the ice cold lake water. The long string of Christmas lights they'd hang from its lower branches added cheer to his heart. He described its relaxing smell, and how it could withstand ice, heat and even flooding.

It was in Lake Michigan where he learned to swim in the summers, and skate in the brutal winters.

People, both young men and women were drawn to him, not just because of his looks, but he had a way of making others feel good about themselves.

In the early days we only saw each other for a few weeks every summer. When school was out, he would stay with us, and his dad.

THE GUISE

At that time my Uncle Ivan lived in a dilapidated trailer behind a junkyard, which was only nine blocks south of our home. He spent his nights working as a correctional officer in the men's jail, and his days as an associate minister at the Methodist Church.

My father was away from home in New Mexico a great deal with his career, therefore when he was home I would follow him around like a baby duckling. If we were eating I would sit and stare at him quietly until he finished his meal. Normally, before he finished reading his newspaper he would tell me about his job, or of his travels out of state.

"Your uncle, the Right Reverend Guise wasn't always a minister you know?" he said looking at me over his reading glasses. My mother would calmly get up and go into the other room, to avoid hearing it.

My father's eyes glistened while he spoke of the days past, which to him were not long ago. I loved hearing him tell of the past, whether it was about his time fighting the Nazis in WWII, freezing in the Korean War, or of my mom's zany offbeat kid brother, my Uncle Ivan.

8

In the early days before he met Helen, my Uncle Ivan dreamed up elaborate business schemes and was able to convince my mother to invest. When my father came into the picture, he was not so easily convinced, and did not believe anything that my uncle said. My uncle was a minstrel, a joker whose thoughts and actions were not rooted in reality, especially when it came to other people's hard earned money.

My dad often summed up the dynamic between my mother and her brother using the analogy of a fable by Aesop; The Ant and the Grasshopper.

During the summer's withering heat the ant works and stores up supplies. The grasshopper uses the summer to play, dance and sing. When the winter snow comes the ant is prepared while the grasshopper has nothing and begs the ant for help. In the story my father insisted my mother was the ant and Uncle I. C. Guise was the grasshopper.

No matter how much my dad tried to explain this to my mom, she always failed to understand his nature and fell for his trickery over and over again...

For starters, there was the bagel shop, which was one of the first ideas that my parents financed for my uncle.

The City of Riverside and its 80,000 residents had, like many small cities at the time, a main street which consisted of businesses to shop for most of the things needed for everyday life. There were two large banks, four supermarkets, a few butcher shops, two bakeries, two pizzerias, four dry cleaners, four shoe stores, and several barber shops. There were three major car dealers that were firmly established on either side of the fifteen mile main street, and two hospitals just beyond each of them. Behind the hospitals were three funeral homes, a bail bondsman, and the county jail which sat at the western end of County Road 90.

My parents signed on the dotted line and rented a small place in the downtown district of the city of Riverside on my uncle's behalf. They purchased all the necessary restaurant equipment, which according to my father was "broke the bank" expensive.

"Guise's Bagels & Bags"

Uncle Ivan's Bagel shop took right off and customers came out of the woodwork to eat his bagels. He made everything fresh from scratch, explained my father. He made his own cream cheese using fresh chives imported from Southern Italy, along with sweet goat's milk. His bagel dough was freshly made the day before baking and he touted this as his secret recipe.

"Bagels & Bags" was the toast of the town !

My father mentioned he decided to make a surprise inspection of the place one Sunday morning. He arrived at "Bagels & Bags" at 0630. He said he never made it inside, due to the line stretching out the door, and halfway around the block. In addition there was nowhere to park.

He told me privately that he thought, "there was no way bagels would sell like that."

When I asked what he meant he would merely say, "You will understand when you are older."

Less than fifteen months later my uncle lost interest in "Bagels and Bags" and let the business fail.

Disappointed bagel customers began calling the house, demanding more bagels, and asking questions about the business. One man even threatened to sue. What was sure, bagel or not, the phone bill, power, rent and taxes still had to be paid by my parents.

This fiasco caused a rift between my mom and dad, and they teetered on permanent separation due to the great loss of money they had incurred. The night after the bagel joint closed, my father left my mom, and stayed away for two months. Meanwhile, my mom had all the restaurant equipment and furniture put in our basement.

My uncle? He took the money he had made and flew to sunny Spain for thirty days with his friend, Mr. Jerome, my father attested while smirking and winking his left eye at me.

My poor mom was left all alone holding the bag, or in this case, the bagel.

Eventually my father came back home, and peace was restored.

The next venture Uncle Ivan undertook was as an offset printer. My mother bought him plate makers, typesetting machines, hundreds of assorted ink jugs, an immense printing press, a massive commercial paper cutter and one thousand reams of assorted paper stock.

Once again my parents reluctantly leased commercial property downtown for him. My father now had proof of why he was skeptical, but to keep the peace relented to my mother trying to help her kid brother.

The printing business?

"Guise's Gawks"

In the fall of 1951 "Guise's Gawks" took off like a bolt out of the blue! My uncle instantly had printing jobs from all over! For the schools he made posters and grade books. For the towns of Horse Neck and Riverside he made banners and flags. For local real-estate brokers he made For Sale signs. For the local residents he skillfully made engraved invitations for bridal showers, weddings, baby showers and bar mitzvah's ! Within one hundred days the county tax office hired him to print all their tax notices.

He came to my father for eighteen consecutive months with $500 repaying him for the bagel shop debacle. It looked as if he had finally found his niche. He hired three assistants to help him, and he was making the company payroll and business expenses, all of which were good signs. Trucks delivered paper daily, and the printing press ran twenty hours a day.

He was a man on the move, and in the spring of 1953 he was featured in the community magazine under the heading "Best New Business." My uncle loved this praise, and he was invited to speak at the Chamber of Commerce two or three times.

This was all news to me, since I knew him only as the Reverend I.C. Guise and never saw him without his clergy uniform, or a long black cassock that he wore all day on Sundays.

Peace had returned between my parents, and a feeling of ease that they had helped him, and that the past was the past.

It was only when the State Bureau of Investigation showed up at our door that things inexorably all went south again. It seems that my uncle was printing counterfeit food stamps, and offering them for sale at a huge discount. For those not familiar with food stamps, they are very similar to currency, but only to be used for food. They are given by the government to low income families, and senior citizens who are strapped for a means to feed themselves.

My uncle skillfully printed up the coupons, in most of the denominations and sold them for cash. If you bought ten $20 coupons, that had a purchasing power of $200, his discounted price was $75. It was essentially like printing up U.S. currency, but at the state level.

The investigators had warrants and probable cause to search "Guises Gawks," his old trailer and even my parents' home on the day Uncle Ivan was arrested.

Uncle Ivan stayed in jail for four months while the Grand Jury deliberated. The case was then sent to the District Attorney to be prosecuted.

LEGATTO THE GREAT

Since he was looking at twenty years in a state prison my parents had no choice but to retain a lawyer.

My father found a lawyer whose office was above a local bakery, his name was Abraham Legatto, Esq.

At the time Mr. Legatto was 70 years old and he had been in legal practice for forty-six years. What was odd was that Legatto didn't advertise and did not have a listing in the phone book. It was assumed when my father called that he had been referred by someone, but he had simply misdialed the phone number.

Legatto was known within the state as a fierce litigator, though later in his career most of his cases rarely went to trial. The few prosecutors that did oppose him in criminal or civil court found themselves severely outmatched no matter the weight of evidence against his client.

Legatto had a unique skill of making small matters within testimony big, and big matters he made so small they disappeared within the minds of jurors.

He explained this skill simply as, "Love." He was gifted at seeing the mind, and understanding the hidden motivations of the opposing counsel, the judge and most of the jurors. This gift combined with pitch, sound pressure, eye attention, glib remarks, phonetics, rate of speech, prosodic silent pauses, intonation and resonance made him one of the best litigators on the Eastern seaboard.

Eleven years earlier, in 1942 Abraham Legatto volunteered to help with the war effort and was commissioned into the US Army's Judge Advocate Generals Corps as a Captain.

With his command of French and Italian he was quickly shipped to the European theater and was placed in the 7th Army under General Patton. He began his military service as a Provost Marshal enforcing discipline within the Army's wartime code of conduct. He accomplished this using court martials of soldiers accused of crimes in the midst of the war.

Later as France was liberated by US forces he was assigned as liaison for the US Army Commanders and local governments for the city of Maisons-Laffitte and Eauplet. Captain Legatto worked with the emerging French underground, which was now liberated and taking control of the new government. He proved very effective at finding the right goods and supplies to help emerging governments.

In recognition of his success, he was promoted and then sent to the city of Palermo, Italy during the invasion of Sicily. His job there was to advise U.S. Army commanders in the best course of action with assisting in the establishment of the new Italian government.

During the invasion there was an issue of inadequate maps that detailed the Italian countryside and many of the essential and smaller seaports. These maps and information were destroyed by the occupying Nazis, as they were driven out.

During this time there were thousands of orphaned children roaming the streets, living within the skeletons of bombed out and condemned buildings, and within the mountainous countryside. It was a serendipitous meeting that Major Legatto had with a precocious twelve year old orphaned boy. This boy's name was Santo Salucci.

Prior to the stifling grip the fascists had on Palermo's local businesses, Santo's father was a thriving fisherman that had a well-established concession providing fresh fish to the local residents. At an early age, and in addition to going to school he would accompany his father in their large boat on late night fishing trips.

As an orphan, he witnessed the U.S. Army fighting their way into the city, block by block. Oddly enough he found kindness from the American soldiers. One in particular was Major Abraham Legatto.

Sandy, as Major Legatto called him, had introduced him to others within the clandestine underground who then provided him with a plethora of useful information, that couldn't have been obtained otherwise.

As the son of a fisherman, Sandy knew the local waterways like the back of his hand. In exchange for hot food and chocolate bars Sandy drew maps of the local waterways, and later provided names and locations of the insurgency of fascists to Major Legatto.

Eventually, Major Legatto made first hand contact with this radical clandestine group that sought to oust the Nazis and Mussolini's National Fascist government. This secret underground group provided him with extremely detailed maps of the area's seaports, and a comprehensive list of the names of Nazi sympathizers. Their help was invaluable to the Allies in expediting the liberation of the area, and Italy as a whole. This aided the military with the command and control needed to stabilize the region, especially the dangerous waterways and ports.

This group is now very well known as, "The Mafia."

THE BIRTH OF LONGBOW

On August 1st 1945 the sun rose upon the Pasqotouk Indian Nation and Taka "tall tree" Longbow, and Dyani Brightwater were already cutting up firewood. This particular day it was a shared task, Taka would position a cut log on the ground and powerfully split it with one mighty swing of his axe. Taka Tall Tree was one of the tallest men of the Pasqotouk and stood well over six foot four inches tall. He had a massive chest, and robust biceps, triceps connecting his bulging shoulders. He had been splitting logs for 40 minutes before dawn. Taka Tall Tree had just removed his shirt revealing his hairless and sweaty skin, before complaining loudly, "This is woman's work!"

Ignoring him, Dyani quietly gathered the split wood, taking large bundles of the oak effortlessly inside the house and laying the pieces near her immense cast iron kitchen stove. Normally this was Dyani's job, especially swinging the axe to split the wood, since Taka had felled the trees in the spring and pulled them all home a full timber at a time with his two sorrel mules, and stacked the long pieces according to length in the back yard.

Taka Tall Tree Longbow would have already been at his engine shop where he repaired and built engines, but today he figured it best he stay home and help Dyani with her house-work since she was in the 297th day of her pregnancy.

Taka Tall Tree Longbow had only 18 months earlier re-turned home from fighting in World War II in the Pacific. At 38 years old he was drafted and in 1943 he was sent to basic train-ing in California . A month after that he was sent to the Pacific with the United States Army.

32 year old Dyani Brightwater wasn't a particularly pret-ty native woman, her dark smoky eyes were too close together, her mesorrhine nose was rather large under her large furrowed forehead, and she had a bony face. But what she lacked in beauty she more than made up for in her clear sighted and unflappable zeal as a mother and wife. She only stood five foot three inches tall, but since her back was wide, had she been taller she would have appeared ungainly instead of stout. No one would dispute how beautiful her hair was, and she took great pride in it and it grew very quickly to incredible length. Her head full of bone straight and healthy black hair would have touched the ground if she had not tied it up. However, now and for the last 11 months it had begun falling out. Her hair loss began very slowly with a few strands here and there, that she found while sweeping the floor. She increasingly began to find strands of her long black hair on her pillow in the mornings, or in the bathtub in the eve-nings. This all wasn't completely unusual and it seemed at times to come with having such long hair. But it had worsened over the past winter when it fell out in clumps. Every morning once Taka was off to work and the children were in school, she would stand in front of the mirror and brush her hair. One particular morning as she was brushing it, she noticed more of her scalp than normal. Instead of hair there were smooth round reddish areas that were without hair. As she closely examined her scalp she sadly discovered many such areas, some the size of a quarter, and others the size of a half dollar. These smooth hairless patch-es continued to multiply across her entire scalp.

Heartbroken, but with no time to be sad over it, she went outside one day with a mirror and with a pair of sewing scis-

17

sors and planned to trim her hair. After balancing the mirror on a porch rail she began trimming it on the sides, then the back, and finally the top. The trimming incredulously revealed more of the hairless punched out red spots on her scalp, which were too numerous to count. With huge tears in her eyes she made twist braids with the longest sections, then used the sewing scissors to cut these sections close to her scalp. Eventually and over the next 45 minutes all her beautiful black hair lay at her feet upon the wooden planks of the porch. She took a white cotton scarf, tightly wrapped it around her head, and went back to her housework.

It was only a matter of days when she glanced in the same mirror noticing that her eyebrows were now disappearing. It was at this exact moment that she knew for sure that she was sick.

The baby was just a few days late from her own calculations and she had delivered three other children for him years ago. Three boys and they were large and strapping at 9, 7 and 5 years old.

The boys had already been fed breakfast and headed to school an hour earlier.

Dyani had already experienced being pregnant and the immense joy and pain of motherhood, however she knew something was different about this child.

Before she knew of his existence she had been at death's door with high fevers that lasted days, followed by chills lasting the same amount of time. It was not long after she cut all her hair off with the sewing scissors and observed that her eyebrows had all fallen out and that large round red bullseye shaped skin rashes appeared across the top of her breasts. As the weeks went by this rash spread to and covered the smooth brown velvety skin of her inner thighs. The only good news was they didn't hurt or ache, but only itched. Her stomach cramped like she was being sawed in half like she had seen at the white circus when she was a girl. Her chest burned like hot coals in the middle of the night which was only relieved by sitting up or standing. Her bowels moved only once a week and they were covered in bright red blood. After the tribal nurse noticed that she had lost all her hair and 30 pounds she personally drove her to town to the white Horse Neck Doctor for his opinion.

She was diagnosed with tuberculosis and a secondary diagnosis of stomach ulcers, and acute kidney stones. The white doctor gave her tons of medicine and told her to go home and rest.

It was a particularly cold, wet and stormy winter in 1945, of which Dyani spent most of it in bed ill and near death. When March arrived the intense cramps turned into the distinct kicking of a baby.

Elijah was a small newborn, and weighed only 6 pounds 3 ounces. It was a normal and quick delivery and he was born in the bathtub of the two bedroom family shack deep within the woods of the proud Pasqotouk Indian Nation at 8:44 a.m. Wednesday, August 1st 1945. The only odd thing about his birth was Elijah didn't cry at birth but simply made gurgling and whistling sounds for his first breaths of life. The midwife was astonished with this, and since she was a Christian advised his parents to give him a Christian name and they did, naming him Elijah Jerimiah Longbow. The midwife and local tribal physician deemed him healthy; despite his diminutive size, he would focus on moving objects in front of him, he passed the Babinski reflex test, would grasp objects placed in his hands, his color was good and his hips flexed well. But Dyani knew that he was not like her other sons.

There was always something very different about Elijah when he was growing up. He was a good student, an obedient and loving son, however he didn't speak a word until he was five years old. He did nod his head a great deal, whistled, shrugged his shoulders, grunted occasionally and even smiled but no words. This never stopped his mother from teaching him their native language, and encouraging her son to play as much as possible, while constantly encouraging him to speak. "Use your words, son" is what she said to him each day, he merely nodded and would occasionally grin or smile at her, but he loved hearing his mother's voice, and it soothed him.

His father, Taka Tall Tree played a huge role in the teaching of the children. He enforced their chores, to help with the cutting of trees, cutting the grass, scraping the stalls, feeding the dogs, and to help with normal day to day tasks of the family. One of the foremost things he did was to speak to them every night of tribal history. He dutifully told them story after story of how they had come to live in "this shack" as he called it in the middle of the woods.

He spoke of days long ago as his father and grandfathers had taught him. The days prior to the White Man arriving on their shores. The stories began the same each night, after they had their evening meal he would sit in his big comfortable chair, the boys quietly and peacefully sat on the hard wooden floor in front of him offering him their complete attention.

He would begin the same each night. "In the earliest time we the proud Pasqotouk, owned and controlled all land around us, 168 days walk in all directions."

When Taka mentioned the name "Pasqotouk" he would hit his fist to his chest, lifting his chin slightly. He spoke of how clean the land, air and water had been, and the abundance of rabbit, deer, and even bear. The Great Taunton River and Horse Neck Bay had an abundance of dolphin, flounder, and blue fish. "The Matipan River had as much crab as we could carry." He described the water fowl, the graceful crane, the squawky and loud migrating geese, and wild duck and their great abundance. The birds of the woods; the quail, the ring neck pheasant, and the grouse all were healthy and plentiful.

"We the Pasqotouk," again lifting the chin and fist to his chest, "We are the masters of the water and of all the lands!"

The boys had heard all of this hundreds of times, but each time they heard their father speak it, they silently filled with joyful pride.

"The white man first appeared on our shores in my great grandfather's, grandfather's time. He came by ship with his weapons of war." When he said weapons he placed the palm of

20

his powerful hand near his mouth and flecked it quickly forward, then he extended his brawny left arm and hand while tilting his head, aiming it at the children and then into the air, only then did he put his hands down and cupped them as if holding a book.

"This weapon and his other weapon were powerful and we fought and still fight today!" The weapons he spoke of were the rifle and holy book of the White Man, the Bible. The mouth or the language of the White Man is one of his great weapons! An additional weapon that came with him was "blood" as Taka touched his sternum in the explanation. He was speaking of tuberculosis, influenza and of course smallpox. "Just being in the vicinity of the white skins the Pasqotouk would get sick and die," he reiterated.

The boys knew the story by heart, and it was always begun the same way each night, but ended at a different point in history.

One of the stories was how they came to live in the place they do now. "This shack was a hasty shelter my father erected when I was a boy," explained Taka. "We proud Longbow lived on the bay in a strong house made of bleached white oak, and we carved and made boats for fishing, boats for war and commerce." He went on to tell of a warm night in 1906 the White Man's police militia came with guns and took their home, beat and raped his mother, and murdered his older brother. Their home was commandeered and usurped by local business owners. The entire family went running for their lives into the night, and wound up in this spot here. "From this place is where my father built this shack very quickly." During this time, he explained, the federal and state government's official policy on the tribes of Natives within the United states was explained in one word, which he had to say in English, "Genocide."

Their beautiful house on the beach was then torn down and their acreage was seized and stolen. Their large boat building workshop and warehouse was burnt to the ground and then bulldozed so not a track nor a trace of it was ever seen again. Fine waterfront homes for rich whites were built in its stead.

These homes and that beach would become part of the town of Hampton, and later with the addition of the stolen Longbow land became "New - Hampton – Beach."

Year after year for the last 500 years the tribe would lose 10- 15 acres of land annually, and their tribal population would decrease by 8%-10 % by untimely death, or young women would just go missing. Those that remained became infertile, or the children died at birth. The missing young women at the time were noticed and heart felt but there was no real empirical data. Every year at least nine young women would be snatched away from this mighty nation.

"They told us of the White Man's court of law, and how we could reclaim our lands using that system. That same system was designed, fashioned and shaped to rob and steal and protect those who did, but they told us it was how we keep our lands safe."

However, no Native could testify against anyone with white skin in any court in the state. He explained, "They are all liars and use the book, and the language to rob, steal , murder us by telling us to love and forgive the criminals, rapists and murderers."

Taka would explain precisely as it was taught to him, that the English language is that of murder and robbery since every word that is spoken or written has at least three different meanings, therefore it is deceptive and anyone who speaks it can never be completely trusted. These lessons were taught in Algonquin, and Taka Tall Tree's use of it was expressive, masterful and musical.

Other nights he would speak of his experiences in the White Man's army fighting the Japanese in the Pacific. These experiences and stories were particularly fresh in his mind, and painful. The stories he told his children were firsthand accounts of battles, weapons, and tactics. For the most part, his stories about the war were no different than any other veteran that served in the United States Army during wartime. However, what was different was how he explained he fought in two wars at the same time. Of course he had experienced bringing war far across the intensely beautiful azure waters of the Pacific to the Japanese. But another war existed concomitantly. The other war he spoke of was how he was treated by his fellow soldiers. He arduously explained that the white troops he served with spoke to him in the most derisive of ways. He was often called "chief," "injun" or worse. Offended by his presence in their midst, they spoke a foul and often repeated sentiment he heard from the white skin: "Dirty Fucking injun. If they have you here fighting with us, we must be truly losing this war!"

Taka explained to his children that the Pasqotouk, and others like them were seen by the White Man as lazy liars that had no other goals or aspirations than laying with his squaw, abusing alcohol and being sloppy. He was told that the Army was no place for him, and he was "just another nigger but with feathers."

At the edge of his seat during this segment of the night's story, Taka was now full of rage and wide eyed while he continued. The children liked this side of their father, it excited them.

With great detail he described some of the natives he had seen on the Pacific atolls, their skin color and of their culture. The whites saw them as primitive and less than human. But despite this he went on to say how the White Man sought to rape the women of these small islands, and plotted to do so. He spoke of how those peoples of the South Pacific were like the Pasqotouk, they owned land, and anyone who owns land will also own war.

He had experienced violence on the ships, and segregation. He was forced to use the toilet or eat only where labeled "Colored Troop Only." Then suddenly he explained he was face to face with the brutal Japanese Army. He had no problem shooting them, or dispatching them with his bayonet but he felt a conflict within his heart. That conflict was that the Japanese didn't rape his mother, or steal his land. His enemy and oppressor was the very man for whom he was helping make war, and very far from his home. He explained much of this to his children, with the hope that they would never be forced to make such a choice fighting for the White Man, who were their actual and true oppressors.

Taka Tall Tree Longbow was an excellent teacher for his beautiful sons, and though all the boys listened to the stories and learned, Elijah was the most moved by them.

Elijah would have vivid dreams where he would be interacting with the characters in his father's story. He would fight the robbers, he would dispatch the rapists, he would restore the stolen lands. These haunting stories and his intense dreams would remain with him the rest of his life.

Elijah never cried a day in his life, he didn't laugh and seldom smiled. He didn't like hugs from his mother like his brothers did privately. His mother would try to hug him and he would worm away from her. Taka would hug him daily and pat the top of his head. He didn't worm away from his father, but never hugged him back. Elijah simply didn't like to be touched.

This caused his brothers, especially his next older brother Tokala who was five years older to constantly touch him, mostly in the form of slaps, pokes and punches. This would always lead to a violent exchange between the two. While Tokala was twice his size and would always get the best of his kid brother, Elijah wouldn't ever stop fighting once he began. No matter how hard he was hit he would come back for more, seemingly immune to pain and he was completely fearless. One day Tokala angrily hit him full force with an axe handle, yet Elijah kept right on fighting.

This earned him a great deal of respect among the older boys, who soon became very protective of their baby brother, though it became more evident every year that *they* were the ones who needed protection from him.

It was thought that perhaps he had brain damage or a birth defect from Taka Longbow's service in the Pacific. He had been perhaps exposed to radioactive dust from the bombs dropped on Japan near the end of the war. If it wasn't radioactive dust then surely it was from the napalm he was exposed to in the flamethrower he carried in Saipan. These theories could never be proven, and during the time there was no one that would even listen to any tribal member's care or concerns about war injuries. The US Government's official policy was that they should be proud that they were *allowed* to fight, bleed and die for the country. Most of the Natives that fought in WWII were in segregated units and fought and died alongside of black troops of that time period. Occasionally they were allowed to fight with white troops if their native tongue could be used to obscure radio transmissions, but to be murdered by their commanders instead of being captured. If they were captured it was thought that they would collude with the Japanese who would then learn their language and be able to decipher their tactical battlefield codes. Their skin tone was briefly examined and if their skin color matched a predetermined lightness test on a chart at the induction center, only then would they be put with the "normal troops." Notwithstanding there were all-Native units within the Army, but they always had a white officer in charge of them.

But most likely it was how sick Dyani was with tuberculosis and the large doses of streptomycin she was given in her first trimester by the Horse Neck doctor.

What became sure was no matter how small statured Elijah Jerimiah was or how little he spoke, he more than made up for it with his sheer physicality.

Dyani signed him up for Little League baseball, which he didn't care for very much but he played to make his mother happy. But when she signed him up for lacrosse she saw young Elijah come alive ! He was as fast or faster than the other boys and just as rough and tough. He also exhibited this nature in boxing and football. Moreover, Elijah excelled in other things that his brothers didn't, including was long distance and cross country running. The other was the board game of chess.

His parents were relieved that he was an ordinary child, but just didn't like speaking, or care to speak. But they learned that when he did speak it was short and to the point and they found that endearing.

In 1951 one of his older brothers was drafted to fight in the Korean War, and sadly lost his life in that terrible conflict. The second oldest child was killed in a hunting accident just 18 months after that.

Both Taka tall tree and Dyani died in 1964 from tick borne fever.

All That remained of the Longbow family were Tokala, Elijah and Elijah's infant Son.

Tokala and Elijah were drafted in 1969 to go to Vietnam. Tokala escaped the draft and moved to North Dakota near the Canadian border and began a family

LEGATTO
THE MAGNIFICENT

In short, Mr. Legatto was a lawyer that could make bricks without straw, and could almost turn water into wine, if given enough time.

The Legatto law firm was accessible only through a back door within The Bear Claw Bakery. Once one walked into the bakery, one would continue to the back of the building. Then proceed up one flight of steps, and at the very rear of the landing hung a small sign that said, "Law Offices."

My father told me that meeting Mr. Legatto was a true pleasure, compared to all the other lawyers he had met.

When he arrived at the top of the steps, he heard typewriters tapping, and a small radio playing Christmas carols.

Two legal secretaries were at their desks and didn't look up when my father entered. A well dressed and fit forty year old man wearing a black tailored suit smiled and said, "Mr. Legatto is expecting you."

He led my father down a long hallway with hundreds or maybe even thousands of legal books neatly stacked in custom white oak bookshelves that were situated floor to ceiling. They finally arrived at a door at the end of the hallway, the man knocked once and swept my father in, before he exited.

Legatto stood and warmly shook my father's hand. He was tall. At six foot six inches he towered over my father like a professional basketball player, and for a man in his 70s he was in remarkable shape. He had a full head of black hair with a few streaks of grey, a fresh haircut and closely shaven.

His tailored robin's egg blue silk shirt fit sharply, and his dark blue silk tie was tied in a double Windsor knot with perfection.

His desk was clean, and nothing sat upon it but a small crystal ashtray, two filigree gold and ivory Monte Blanc pens and a blank yellow legal pad.

Legatto offered a seat and elegantly waited for my dad to sit before returning to his leather desk chair.

Mr. Legatto was in possession of an unusually warm and welcoming demeanor. There was a je ne sais quoi within the tone of his voice and a deeply calming confidence that poured from his eyes and his mannerisms recalled my father.

He went on to say that the attorney was smooth and soothing, not in a contrived manner, but the natural way in which he spoke, not to mention the smell of the fresh baked bread that gently wafted up from the downstairs bakery.

After only a few moments of their meeting he realized that Legatto had served in WWII. Not only that but they were both combat veterans, fellow Commissioned Officers and they had both served in the 7th Army under Patton in Europe.

The two veterans spoke of the war for several minutes before my father got to the point of his visit.

As my father explained to Mr. Legatto, there were many issues afoot since Ivan's arrest that were plaguing him. Number one, his brother-in-law was facing at least twenty years in the state prison for counterfeiting and fraud, which was affecting his wife's emotional health.

Number two, he and his wife were on the hook to pay the rent for "Guise's Gawks" since they had signed the rental lease agreement for I.C. Guise, and this was affecting his mental health and peace of mind, not to mention the financial strain.

Legatto listened intently, and scribbled a few notes on a yellow legal pad while my father spoke.

My father said that he was also being forced to make the payments for the loan on the printing presses and all the equipment. This expensive equipment was locked away in the building and they were unable to even inspect it due to the police boarding up the place.

Unlike the other attorneys my father had spoken with about this case, Legatto promised a speedy resolution, and with his voice he conveyed confidence and complete reassurance.

Of course, that would come at a cost. The staggering price tag of his services would force my father to remortgage our family home.

Days later my father met with the chief loan officer at Riverside Savings and Loan, and applied for a second mortgage on our house. It was a routine transaction that would involve a survey of our property and an appraisal. This process took only four working days, after which my father was issued a check in the amount of $27,000. He gave most if not all of it to the Legatto Law Firm immediately.

Once retained, the Legatto Law Firm got right to work that very night on the criminal case.

Over the next five nights the state's witness list was replaced with a single sheet of paper that said "See Attached." However there were no other pages to follow, or attached.

The state's star witness in the case suddenly was unable to remember and denied ever going to "Guise's Gawks" for any reason. Her written deposition was conveniently ruined with dark brown coffee stains.

When she was subpoenaed to reappear for a new deposition a local physician diagnosed her as Non Compos Mentis.

The plates used to print the counterfeit food coupons that had sat securely in the police evidence room were now engraved plates for the printing of bagel menus, and county tax notices. The confiscated counterfeit food stamps that were held in the same evidence locker were now genuine food stamps.

In addition, most of the stenography from the Grand Jury deposition was lost, and the audio recording became severely damaged from an overhead sewer pipe.

It was only after these events occurred that Mr. Legatto advised the court that he was representing the Defendant Mr. Ivan Conrad Guise. The very next thing he did was to file a motion of discovery with the court.

Discovery is when the state willingly provides a copy of the evidence that will be used in court against a defendant to their lawyer.

Days later and responding to the discovery motion the state produced a copy of all of their evidence against Ivan Conrad Guise.

Via certified messenger, copies of all the state's evidence arrived at the Legatto Law Firm.

Mr. Legatto and his team stood examining what the state had produced as evidence against their newest client. It was as follows: a printing plate to print bagel menus, a witness list without any names and only the words "See Attached," copies of three $1 legitimate food stamps, a severely damaged deposition, and the audio recording of the deposed witness was a fuzzy recording of Bing Crosby singing "White Christmas."

Legatto filed a motion for Habeas Corpus and Uncle Ivan was released from county jail the next morning. This made my mom weep for hours with happiness and relief.

Later that week Mr. Legatto filed a motion to have the entire case thrown out, due to lack of evidence. That motion was sustained and the case was dismissed with prejudice along with the court's most sincere apology.

The Legatto Law Firm then turned their attention to the civil case.

Late one Sunday night the original commercial lease that my parents had signed for "Guise's Gawks" was slightly altered. This alteration was the simple addition of a single sentence within the Mutual Waiver Of Subrogation section of the lease.

Instead of this clause saying; "Lessor shall not be responsible for loss for any reason," it now said; "Lessor shall be responsible for loss and further shall indemnify the lessee for any losses." This page was placed in the official file cabinet of the owner of the building, and the law office of the building owner.

The Legatto Law firm sued the building owner for the loss of use from the police action. The building owner quickly settled and paid my parents for the money they had lost over the four months "Guise's Gawks" sat boarded up and closed.

My parents would spend the next 11 years repaying the Riverside Savings and Loan Company and rebuilding their savings account.

NEARER MY GOD, TO THEE

Once he was released from jail after four long months and learning that all of the charges had been dropped against him, my uncle declared that this was a miracle! He would now be going into the ministry.

In the fall of 1954 my uncle moved to Columbiana Ohio to begin his ministerial studies at the state university.

He did this via The Serviceman's Readjustment Act of 1952 which gave money to veterans to further their education. Of course, Uncle Ivan was no veteran, he had used his printing business to simply produce all the forms to make him appear so. This skill (more than a little ironic) was also how he had escaped the draft in the first place. He had forged medical documents that made him appear severely infirmed from a military training accident and that he had been medically discharged from the New Jersey National Guard. These documents were sent to the local draft board with all the correct stamps and signatures. He was never investigated for draft dodging, which speaks to the level of his document forging skills.

One forged document he had stashed away in our basement was a deed for three acres of beachfront land on the Pasqotouk Indian Reservation. This deed had been adroitly printed using the correct paper, and contained all the correct county stamps and official seals and signatures. He also printed up several years of property tax notices for this land, all marked paid.

I personally could have never imagined my uncle able to commit such skillful crimes. When he came to our house for dinner from time to time, he was light hearted, laughed and told jokes all evening. His jokes were droll and on occasion risqué.

In my formative years my father tried his very best to keep me away from him when he came to the house, which was one of those things I never completely understood.

The basement of our home was replete with a commercial bagel oven, a massive printing press and all sorts of furniture -- painful reminders of my uncle's tomfoolery. My parents hated to go into the basement of our home because it brought to mind all the money they had wasted on my uncle.

My uncle's ministry took right off due to his quick witted gift of gab, and his smooth singing voice.

I remember my mom taking me to one of his *Concerts of Joy*, as he called them. The one we went to was on a cool Sunday afternoon down at Devil's Lake.

The Devil's Lake area of town was in the midst of white flight, as home ownership had plummeted. The families that remained there were all gainfully employed and were largely business owners on Main Street.

Forty gray metal folding chairs with "Albert's Funeral Home" written on the back on them in green block letters were set up. A tent had been erected, with an eight foot folding table across the front. Upon the table sat a resplendent 36" golden cross, that had come up missing from the Catholic Church three months earlier.

Chairs began filling up, while a young man in a well-tailored solid blue suit directed my mother and I where to sit.

My uncle appeared in a foppish kelly green three piece suit, white shirt and silver tie. Covering his shoulders was a waist length silver lame cape.

His small quick steps made it seem like he was floating across the black plastic carpet. Once he arrived in front of the table, he kneeled at the cross in prayer. This silent prayer lasted ten minutes and until it was quiet and the crowd of forty was no longer clamoring.

A young man appeared and removed my uncle's cape in a carefully orchestrated act, after which he stood. My uncle's face was distorted and trance-like. He stood staring into the top of the tent and after a few more minutes at last he began speaking.

He spoke at first in a normal conversational voice, which gradually increased until his voice resonated across Devil's Lake. I had no idea the man had such a smooth powerful voice.

With arms lifted he remonstrated:

"The Lord is ever ready"

"You never go into a problem alone, thy Lord is with thee"

"Nearer my God to thee, only when you give your money to me"

"There is not fruit in the sky, or in the by and by. It's right here right now"

After he said this, he broke into song!

His favorite song while making direct eye contact with everyone, including my mother and I was: "Blessed Assurance."

His singing wasn't ordinary, it was ritardando at 1/8 or less of the song's normal tempo, while he soulfully dragged out each syllable of each lyric and musical note making them harmonically hang in midair for many seconds. After he finished each extended note it melted into the next lyric and note which he also held for ten to twelve seconds.

He would sing until there wasn't a dry eye in the place, or someone passed out. If this didn't happen within fifteen minutes, which was rare, he would merge into "We Are Marching to Zion!" Then he would bring it all on home with "Just a Closer Walk with Thee." He sang this song with the same extremely slow tempo as the others. Skillfully slowing it to 1/16 bar, stretching every note, making the song last for at least fifteen minutes.

This routine was akin to a rock opera and seemed to have been rehearsed a thousand times by my uncle and the young men. Their timing, pageantry and presence was impeccable.

In later concerts he was said to have an electric piano, and he would holy dance.

During the last song, one of the young male ushers would pass an old fishing bucket around while onlookers would pour in donations.

As the years passed he was often asked to preach and sing at funerals, weddings, or minister to the sick, all of which was quick cash, some of which he used to repay my parents.

MONTE CUCCIO

While the second world war in Europe had seemingly just begun less than twenty four months earlier for the Americans, war had been raging for Santo Salucci and his parents for 12 excruciating years. The year of Santo's birth, in 1930 Benito Mussolini had ravaged Italy and had gone about destroying every vestige of democracy within the country for almost a decade. He declared himself Il Duce and dictator of all of Italy. He and his paramilitary fascist party invaded Abyssinia in 1935 while he at the same time they murdered and killed their own countrymen who openly or secretly defied fascism. Within Palermo there were death squads called the OVRA which were secret police and Black Shirts that went street by street sweeping and killing any opposition to Il Duce.

Because of this, Santo had never known peace or tranquility. He had never played games like normal children, he had only known fear, death and oppression. However, it was of these cruel things where he made his boyhood games.

Once his older brother Marcello disappeared on his way to school one day, Santo's parents did something unspeakable; they stopped sending him to school. Truancy was strictly enforced, school at that time was 100% fascist propaganda, and the loyalty to the state was all that was taught, once the free press was curtailed.

While all this was going on his father still made his living fishing and was allowed to sell his catch at market for many years while he pretended to embrace the new government. Santo and his father spent much time together on their boat at night fishing and he would question his father about the government and the murderous Carabinieri that roamed the countryside. He asked his father "Why" a great deal, and his father would simply reply, "Niente che valga la Pena di Avere e Facile," nothing worth having comes easy. One of the other sayings his father would quote about life during this time was, "Mal commune mezzo gaudio," a shared trouble is a half joy. These times with his father were happy times, and he looked up to and admired his father's strength and wisdom.

His mother made clothes for him, cooked and taught him, and loved him all the while fearing what the future held for them all. His parents were brave, strong and proud people, and they instilled a certain self-reliance in their only remaining child, young Santo.

In 1940 and responding to a truancy complaint from the school, a squad of OVRA came to the Salucci household late one night. A scuffle ensued between Pescatore Salucci and the secret police, in which Salucci was shot and killed. Only a few moments later two more gunshots rang out, marking the end of Santo's mother. Young Santo ran into the night for his life. He went to several doors and knocked but no one, not one neighbor opened the door to help him. The words from within were simply "Via !" Finally, he nestled into a doorway and waited until dawn. It was an hour before dawn when he heard a door unlatch and open slightly, and then he hears the raspy voice of an old woman, "Andare in montagna" then the door closed and re latched. A few moments later he heard the voice again "Va Via."

Young Santo ran and didn't stop until he got to the foothills on the outskirts of the city as the sun was rising.

He stood gazing at the rugged cloud piercing peaks of Monte Cuccio now bathed in myriad breathtakingly beautiful hues of orange, magentas and red.

Part of the vast Apennines mountain range, Monte Cuccio had watched over the city of Palermo for eons of time. It had stood with its grandeur before there was a Sicily, before Italy itself, and probably before the Mediterranean sea was formed with its craggy and jagged peaks that punctured the sky.

It is said this is the exact place where the myth of Icarus was born. Its peak soared to well over 3,500 feet above sea level, and often it was obscured by mystic swirling grey clouds. It was a place easily seen from all points of the city, but many places upon the mountain were totally inaccessible. Many of its hidden features were forests of rare fragrant trees, immense grass covered valleys, breathtaking multi-mile chasms and vast rocky escarpments.

Wild mountain goats frolicked and played upon prodigious and toweringly steep scree fields created by falling stones the size of Buicks that precariously lay wobbling and unsteady. Midway down, the rocks were small and razor sharp and would roll and slide down the steep inclines in deadly bunches.

It was a paradox, though plainly seen by all from a hundred miles away, Monte Cuccio kept her secrets safely hidden.

Santo walked and climbed over sharp rocks, following goat paths all that day. The higher he climbed the wetter everything became. Sharp rocks were now also slippery. The steep and scabrous terrain began piercing his tender young hands and torso as he climbed; not only that, a cold stinging wind began to blow from the west which further inhibited his ascent. It was at sunset when a smooth limestone outcropping appeared. It was covered on three sides and provided shelter from the howling winds where he laid and immediately fell asleep shivering and in sheer exhaustion.

The winds blustered intensely all night and into the next morning while Santo curled himself into a ball and slept in his small shelter. Once the powerful winds calmed, the clouds departed and bright sunlight began to warm him. It was only then that Santo cared to look down, and what he witnessed would have astonished a veteran climber. His limestone shelter was perched at a dizzying 1,800 feet above the sea, which lay in a panoramic vista far below him. The boats out to sea appeared as ants upon a luscious blue green tapestry, beside the city of Palermo small enough to fit inside a thimble. Had he kept looking fear would have made his unknown journey untenable, so he never looked down again.

That morning he continued the climbing upwards. It would be two more full days and nights of climbing before he found a small water puddle within a limestone plate that had formed from a spring further up from which he instantly stuck his face in and lapped it up, slowly at first then ravenously. Refreshed from this, he climbed a bit further and it was there in a grassy patch he discovered a small mint plant. After picking the leaves and putting them to his nose to smell them, he plucked a few more leaves and put them all in his mouth. He chewed them a few times which began the process of digestion. The first few he swallowed, the others he held in the corner of his cheek. The moment he did this, the sugars from the leaves were released and quickly entered his bloodstream. He began to warm, and his dull thinking began to dissipate. The pangs from hunger began to ease, and the oils from the plant soothed the pain he had felt for a few days near his shoulder.

Santo took all of the leaves and stuffed them in one of his pockets before his journey continued. It was only luck but Santo had discovered a worn path where he was able to walk. He moved normally for the first time since he had fled from the doorways to the mountain, and it felt good walking upright. It was then that he noticed his shoes, and how they began to fall apart. The leather soles were scarred and cut up, to the point where the upper part of his left shoe separated from the lower part. In despair he sat on the cold ground and took off both shoes. He noticed only then that the bottoms of his feet were bleeding.

This path was on the southern facing slope of Monte Cuccio and warm moist air came up from the Mediterranean Sea offering protection from the strong penetrating winds of the north. He followed this warmly lit and inviting path an entire day before he found a confluence of rocks and flowering trees that formed a shelter on three sides, and that was where he collapsed. Santo fell into a deep sleep while the sun set and a dense fog fell over the area. The gauzy mist penetrated the rocky earth and obscured every feature around him. This thick blanketing haze was warm, and though it made navigation impossible, it soothed young Santo and allowed him to slip into a deep sleep which was precisely what he needed. Nestled within this confluence of rocks is where he would stay for the next two days.

All Santo had with him when he fled his home were the clothes on his back, a small tin Saint Benedict's medallion, prayer card and round black and white picture of his mother.

A heavily armed band of partisans were on patrol, and noticed fresh footprints, parts of shoes, and bloody toe prints which they followed right to the place where he lay.

Finding him unresponsive they initially thought he was dead, when in fact he was still narrowly clinging to life. They urgently carried him back to their group, in hopes of saving him.

Their impenetrable rocky cave stronghold was deep within the mountainous cliffs of Monte Cuccio.

Not only was he frail and sick, but Santo had sustained a fractured collarbone from a fall while climbing up the side of a steep cliff. A young woman was placed in charge of caring for him. Her name was Anna Donatto. Anna had escaped from the clutches of the jail where she and her younger sister had been kidnaped and held illegally by the Carabinieri.

She didn't speak of what happened to her in that jail cell, but whatever happened was dreadful, and it cost the life of her baby sister who at the time was merely 16 years old.

Anna helped the twenty-three member group in all ways, she would go on hunting parties, or robbing raids, and she also did some cooking , meal preps and was in charge of first aid. Anna had received an education in Apothecary from her father who had been the local chemist of her town, and she used this training to help her injured paisons.

There was a tincture she made from the oil of Chive. This vibrant green and fragrant oil would be applied topically to injuries, or it could be taken internally. If the injuries were not superficial she would mix the green chive oil with a tincture of the milk from a poppy flower. A small cut in the long stem plant's bulb at dawn, would yield ¼ of an ounce of narcotic milk by dusk. She would heat these two substances over hot coals from the fire, and once they cooled she would add a drop to an open wound, then sew it closed. She removed bullets and set broken bones. In Santo's case she mixed this tincture with warm sweet goat's milk which she made him drink twice a day while he recovered. This removed all of his pain and allowed the young boy to sleep.

He suffered from extreme fever and chills for weeks after he was found. Anna tended to the boy around the clock, with medicine, cool towels and warm blankets. Her soothing voice and her kind eyes, not to mention her great beauty was the first thing Santo saw and heard while he was in and out of consciousness.

She nursed young Santo back to health with her tender loving care, and soothed his frayed nerves with her motherly kindness.

The fretful night he was awakened by his mother, to get up out of bed, she got him dressed and put his coat on, with her picture and Saint Benedict's medallion and prayer card within a pocket during the OVRA's invasion of their home. Seeing his mother shot and killed, to the doorways, to climbing the goat paths were all one huge blur to Santo and his young memory. He wondered if Anna was real, or if he had been shot and killed or frozen to death in the hills. He would suffer with these memories for the rest of his life.

Santo was welcomed and quickly made part of the group, only after thoroughly being questioned to find out how and why he was alone and without his own family. Many of the other young ones there had lost their families in similar ways.

Since he was off his feet for a month during his recovery the first thing she taught him was the game of chess.

Santo became so proficient with the game of chess he began playing the leader of the group.

The man in charge was 55 year old Don Biagateao.

Don Biagateao was covered in ruddy olive hue Mediterranean skin. He was of average height and weight, at 5 foot 9 inches and 180 pounds. His curly salt and pepper hair was cut close, but thinning slightly revealing a tanned and healthy scalp. The climbing he had been forced to do while living in exile had greatly strengthened his arms and legs while slimming his waist. An added bonus was the thin mountain air had strengthened his heart and lungs, and at 55 Don Biagateao was as strong as a bull and it showed.

Don Biagateao had a penchant for the dramatic. He used his hands when he spoke, and waved his arms a great deal along with the pitch of his voice when in public. Privately he spoke in whispers and stood unusually close to everyone he spoke to. The Don had a beautiful smile and loved to laugh a great deal, but normally only when it was appropriate. His personality was balanced but it could be deceiving. The bottom line was he was a veteran of World War I and he was in his element living in the mountains and loved every moment of it. Not just being in charge, but those of whom he was in charge. He put the elite group together and controlled them by allowing them to think they were not controlled, which illustrated his brilliance.

Don Biagateao was actually a heart-broken man deep inside, from the loss of his entire family from way back before Mussolini. His mother and father were both murdered, and he had lost his sister and his two brothers to political violence. He had built a brand new family in Gangi, and they were snatched away by Cesare Mori, and he would have his revenge. However he kept this to himself, and never revealed this to a soul.

Antonio Biagateao was raised by his paternal grandparents in Gangi, Sicily. He had served in the first world war while in his early 20s. He had fought against the Hungarians and the Austrians in a special unit called the Alpini. It was in this unit in World War I where he learned mountain tactics and warfare, and he learned much of the German, Hungarian and Turkish languages.

His grandfather was a butcher in town, well liked and extremely respected. He knew of war, he knew of struggle and masterfully understood compromise.

His word was law, however he was affable and led the group by example. He did however maintain a strict hierarchy within the group, and it was structured similar to a military organization, with the older paisons holding the leadership positions. A group of seven boys ranging from 14 to 21 years old were the infantry unit called the "Riservarsi" and were his pride and joy. He was charismatic and cool under pressure and spoke in low tones, and never yelled or even lost his temper with those in his group. However, out on the road and with the Carabinieri or the OVRA it was a different story.

Don Biagateao taught Santo the stratagems of the game, and its subtle nuances. As he advanced into a formidable chess player he began to see the allegories and the bigger picture of what was going on in his country. Who were the pawns, who were the knights, who was king and all of the roles and sacrifices needed to win the game. Occasionally and over the course of the three years he'd spend with his new family he sometimes beat Don Biagateao at chess. Don Biagateao loved and praised him for his ability to beat him.

After a few games of chess Don Biagateao would tell young Santo of his life growing up, and of his grandfather who had spent a great deal of time with him during his childhood. He told the story of how his grandfather had worked early on with a man named Don Cologne before becoming a butcher.

Don Cologne was a land owner and possessed many hundreds of horses and grew lemon trees in Bisacquino. There were immense fields of trees, as far as the eye could see he explained. His grandfather worked with a family named Russo that protected all of the trees and livestock from thieves. Lemons at the time were a cash crop and every single ship without fail, that arrived to their shores needed lemons for journeys home, which made them in great demand. Don Cologne became one of the richest men in all of the South, he explained. As Don Cologne got richer he didn't provide as he should have for his workers who began to steal his lemons, and occasionally a horse just to survive. There were so many trees that if one just took three lemons from each tree, and one from the ground below it would score a massive fortune at the market.

One day his grandfather and a member of the Russo family, Alphonse Russo, followed a band of thieves that had done just that, stolen a few lemons from each tree and they followed them to the seaport. There were 30 stolen horses, mules and donkeys that pulled 15 cart loads of lemons, many thousands of them. Once they got to the market they were intercepted by his grandfather and Alphonse Russo, and after some gunfire they robbed the robbers. There was a conversation between his grandfather and Russo that they should sell the lemons back to Don Cologne, but they decided to sell him his horses back and they went on to sell the lemons to a fleet of Portuguese and British ships for gold. It was so much gold that they split it between them and sold Don Cologne's own mules, horses and donkeys back to him. They grew even richer from the resale of the animals.

With this fortune split between them , Alphonse Russo left for the United States, and his grandfather opened his own farm where he butchered and sold the meat locally. Later, Don Cologne was run out of Sicily by bandits and he returned back to the Northern part of the country.

Santo loved hearing these stories from Don Biagateao, and the colorful way in which he told them.

Though he was too young and weak to be part of the "Riservarsi," Don Biagateao knew he could one day be perfect for this subgroup's leader due to his extreme intelligence. Santo was Don Biagateao's favorite Paison, though he was very careful to not show it openly. It was difficult for anyone not to like Santo, his eyes were bright and wide, and his hair was the color of the sunset on a spring day. He was engaging and showed great respect for his elders.

The cave wasn't dark or cold, its opening faced south and the rising sun from the east provided warming light in the mornings. The evening sun as it set gave a sense of stillness for the approaching night.

This band of outlaws identified themselves as freedom fighters, and sought to disrupt and oust the fascist regime, but they were actually the remaining elements of the powerful Cosa Nostra from the Southeastern township of Gangi, Sicily. They had fled their town and even their own former mountain hideout of Madonie to the safety of these remote rocky cliffs after Benito Mussolini declared war on all of the Cosa Nostra just years prior. Mussolini appointed a man named Cesare Mori to wage this war, and murdered tens of thousands of members of the Cosa Nostra causing them to flee into the hills, or leave the country. This act was like the children's game whack a mole, while Mori reduced the Cosa Nostra in Sicily , they popped up in many other places like Turkey, Greece and of course the United States.

This was Santo's new family.

The cave complex had wooden chairs, tables, a few carpets and in the center a huge hearth. There was a hot fire, with food cooking all the time, blankets, warm clothes, and best of all love. They roasted goats, pheasant, lambs and occasionally a calf on Sunday. There was a mountain spring for fresh water, and a bevy of wild plants that grew nearby. Pantelleria capers, sage, garlic and mint. Their cave had three small generators, many stolen two-way radios, and a huge cache of stolen military weapons.

There were only three ways up by foot, and one way up the opposite side's 2,520 foot sheer rock cliff via ropes. In the day you could see the approach of Carabinieri, and at night they needed lights to see and were easily spotted by the group's lookouts.

There was safety from the Black Shirt Fascists , the OVRA and all of the Carabinieri, on Monte Cuccio since it was only accessible by climbing and not by motorized vehicles.

What this group loved about Santo was he taught and showed a new way to their cave stronghold, previously unknown. This small unseen pathway could have led to an armed invasion. Santo had keen powers of observation even at the age of 10 years old.

He and the other young boys would have contests to see how fast they could go up, or go down the small paths to their stronghold. They would also measure how far their guns would shoot to predetermined points on the path. A 200 year old Cork Oak tree grew wide and tall 158 meters away and 75 meters straight down from a lookout post. It was wedged between two large boulders, and a small path from water runoff was the only access up. One of the older boys using his Enfield rifle could shoot the rocks near the tree with great accuracy, while pretending a Carabinieri was approaching. It was all just a fun game to them. Don Biagateao taught them how to emplace their rifles to allow them to night fire with deadly accuracy. It involved placing six wooden stakes into the ground forming a cradle, and laying the rifle within allowed precise shooting in dark, fog or rain since no aiming would be required. There were 28 such emplacements around their stronghold, with double as many preloaded rifles that lay at the ready.

One of the very first things that young Santo was given other than a water canteen, and small folding knife was a pistol. It was a 1907 Portuguese Savage .32 caliber in good working order. He was also given its smooth black leather holster and two magazines.

Twice a week he would target practice with it, and eventually got very skilled with firing it with great speed and precision. Part of his training was its disassembly, cleaning and caring for it. He took great pride in his pistol, the leather holster and even the small knife which he cleaned daily.

From time to time, he and his fellow partisans would rob and steal from the Carabinieri barracks or just hold them up on the road. They'd take food, ammunition, and anything else they found useful or that would be in their possession. Often they would take their clothes and leave them naked on the road, and sometimes they would shoot them, or both. One of the most fun and entertaining things was to order the Carabinieri to take off their uniforms. Most would resist carrying out this order, even at gunpoint. Anna or one of the boys would then shoot one of them in the liver, and while he lay screaming they would repeat the order. They all would gladly then take off their clothes, normally to their underpants. A few shots at their feet helped persuade them to take off the rest of their clothes.

Once they were completely naked, Don Biagateao would appear with his Enfield rifle slung over his shoulder, smiling as he pretended to be their friend disagreeing with their nudity and how they had been treated. He would return one of them their uniform and ask him to get dressed and to "cover up." Once one of them redressed is when he would flip the script.

One of the other younger partisans and Don Biagateao would pretend to argue on the procedure of the robbery. The other man would say, "They must be naked!" Don Biagateao would insist the Carabinieri must be dressed ! This act would last a few moments before Don Biagateao would relent to them being nude, by just shrugging his shoulders.

He then would assure them in his most soothing manner that their clothes would be returned immediately after they answered a few harmless questions.

He affably asked them a few innocuous questions, like their name, which town they were from, or of local area news. He would make polite conversation about the weather, or even mention the names of people he knew in the towns they were from. He would tell them he was in ill health, and would rub his neck or his back while grimacing and complaining of pain or stiffness in his joints. He would complain that all this robbing was the idea of the younger men of the group and there was no need for it.

Once he had built their trust and perhaps even their sympathy, Don Biagateao would then flip the script again. This time though he would become intolerant with their answers and insist that they were not telling the truth. Mercurial Don Biagateao suddenly became angry, and transformed from an infirmed old man into a wild savage.

Again the scripted play continued, and the paison that had insisted nudity would pretend to try to calm Don Biagateao. The paison would insist that the Carabinieri were just doing their job, and mention the good work they were doing, and that they should be allowed to go on their way. Don Biagateao would not calm down during this, but only become more incensed. The paison would then shrug and say, "Non mi va," or, "I'm not cool with it."

Don Biagateao would then take out his cherished German Luger, and continue his truculent questioning at close quarter gunpoint.

He would demand information on plans of attack or searches in the future, or what was known about them by the Carabinieri.

He became a madman, unhinged with his questioning, yelling and screaming the names of his murdered family and accused those particular Carabinieri of killing them!

Within the eyes of one of them he'd see fear, or smell it. Only then he held his pistol inches away from the genitals of the man being questioned.

At other times, instead of his Luger he would skillfully and quickly pull out his nine inch razor sharp knife and make small cuts to the naked man being questioned. He wouldn't cut the man in random places, he would cut what he called "Le Zone

Verita" or the areas of truth. The soft armpit, the mid biceps, the dorsum of the foot, the bottom of the foot, the Achille's tendon, behind the knee, the ears, the soft tender waistline below the navel, and of course the center of the testicles. Only in these places he made an inch long slice with his knife, if he felt truth wasn't being told, or often even if it was being told.

Once he was satisfied, one man lay gut shot, another lay bleeding in agony, he would fire shots at their feet, making them dance while his fellow paisons all cheered! This cheer marked the beginning of the final act of the scripted charade. They would gather all their weapons, uniforms, fuel, vehicle batteries, money and identification papers and make the arduous trip back to their stronghold. Four heavily armed older boys "Riservarsi" were always left out of view and once the group was safely on their way, they machine gunned the Carabinieri making an end of them. Then they carefully picked up all their cartridge casings, and used shrubs to obscure any footprints left behind. They would take a different path back to the stronghold once they were sure they were not being followed.

Santo sought to become a member of this elite group, however he was not yet strong or fast enough. Part of the test to become part of this, other than being 13 years old was to carry a .30 caliber machine gun, 500 rounds of ammunition, one Enfield rifle with 100 rounds of ammunition, a food pack and four full water canteens down the steep western side of the mountain, set it all up, then disassemble it and carry if back up within 10 minutes. At the time Santo couldn't even lift the machine gun. He thought of his father's saying, "Niente che valga la Pena di Avere e Facile"

But young Santo enjoyed the robbing parties more than anything else. He loved seeing the brutes that had murdered his parents and stolen all of his family's possessions turn into sniveling scared "Granchi Codardi" from the point of his pistol.

Once the fun and robbing was over with for the day there would be music, food, wine and some dancing. After Anna put

49

the children to bed for the night, the older members of the group including the "Riservasi" would sit and speak of their families and what they thought the future held for them. They knew what was happening in Europe and the rest of the world during these times by listening to the BBC radio broadcasts, but normally only once the children were asleep.

This and other hold-ups became a fun game and past time for young Santo. If they stopped locals that had fresh food, instead of robbing them they would purchase their entire load from them, or a large portion of it. Then as a gesture of friendship Don Biagateao would pay them more than they would have made from it at the market. This simple act garnered empathy for those of the Cosa Nostra that made their homes in the remote mountain regions. This feeling could not be further illustrated than by the continued addition to their group by those seeking escape from the oppressive Carabinieri.

Every few months one or two young men would present with a white handkerchief into the goat paths and rocky cliffs. They were met at gunpoint and thoroughly questioned, and sometimes they would be allowed to join. Other times they were deemed "traditore Grancho" or "Granchi Traditori" and sent away, or occasionally they would be placed in a pot, which is where crabs are best kept .

One of the secrets Santo was taught about traitorous crabs , was that they talk a great deal. He learned even when questioned at times it's best to say little or nothing. You certainly don't go about attempting to answer questions that you know nothing about, but instead stand firm in silence. In this you let your eyes speak for you, as they *always* spoke truth.

From time to time, they would meet a brave Carabinieri who would refuse to answer any questions. He would leer at the eyes of the questioner despite the fact that a gun was placed in his face. He wouldn't see the gun, but only the eyes of the man with the gun. When this occurred though it was extremely rare, they would let this man live. They never murdered a brave man, once he was disarmed citing "E Uno di Noi," "he is one of us."

They would take this man's identification papers, and allow him to go on his way. In the many years of living off the grid there had only been two such men. Brave men had simply become a thing of the past.

A time came in the cold and brutal January of 1943 when a company of Nazi infantryman came up the road heading for the city of Palermo. The lookouts, and the "Riservasi" reported to Don Biagateao, who then came out to look at them himself. They were very well equipped with the latest implements of war. This was the Nazi regular army coming in to bolster the Italian army. The younger men sought plans to rob them, however Don Biagateao expressly forbade any such action from his group. He instead planned to kidnap one or two of the Nazi regulars during the night.

For many weeks Don Biagateao and the other senior members of the group planned this action. One night not long afterwards they managed to snatch not two soldiers but three Nazi regulars. They were quickly and quietly overpowered, bound and gagged and taken to a remote area far from the stronghold.

They followed the same script of making the men naked before questioning them.

Don Biagateao came feebly limping out from behind a boulder smiling, and introduced himself in German to the Nazis. He told them what an honor it was to meet them, and have them in his beautiful country before asking them their names and where they were from. The Nazi's were surprised to hear their language spoken so well, and were equally reassured hearing it spoken with an Austrian accent.

One soldier was a Captain, the other a Major and the third was a senior sergeant. Don Biagateao complained to the officers of his aches and pains. He held out the palms of his hands and told them how weak he had become and infirmed with age and arthritis. He went on to tell them he didn't sleep at night, but found himself drifting off to sleep during the day, while he needed to be awake. He complained to them about the weather and how it disagreed with him. While he did this he examined their eyes. Of course these soldiers were in the prime of their lives at twenty-five to thirty years old and strong! He assured them that he only had a few harmless questions and their uniforms and coats would be promptly returned and they would be back on their way.

Don Biagateao knew immediately that these men were much different than the Carabinieri. The look in their eyes revealed the horrible things they had seen and done. These three soldiers were members of the elite Schutzstaffe which he deduced by examining their all black uniforms. The major's uniform had the Iron Cross, third class hanging from a breast pocket. He closely examined the documents they had in their possession, and he deduced that they had just completed rounding up Jews in Greece only days before, and were returning to their garrison.

When Don Biagateao politely asked the older Nazi major his whereabouts just days before, and of his mission in Italy the major spit in his face and called him a "juden liebhaben" or "Jew Lover!" Don Biagateao didn't wipe the spit from his face, he merely smiled and used the back of his hand to wipe the saliva from his eyes. He then dipped his pinky into the saliva and put it to the tip of his tongue while he smiled and nodded his head agreeably and said, "Carne mi Maiale" or " Pork." The moment he said this there was a boisterous guffaw from all the Paisons.

Hearing this Don Biagateao sprang to life, he no longer limped, his voice became youthful and strong as he skillfully hogtied one of them, crab tied another, and the third was meticulously shrimp tied. A small fire was stoked, and two Nazi bayonets were placed within. These blades would be used later on to cauterize their wounds.

He knew from all of his war years that a naked man being held at gunpoint in freezing cold whose mouth wasn't dry and had enough gall and saliva to spit in his face was by far the bravest of them.

The "Riservasi" sat or lay the Nazis facing each other in a semi-circle. While they were positioned near the fire, he said, "Come my German brothers toward the warming fire."

There was utter silence from the entire group while a few stood guarding the captured soldiers, and the others were fanned out and watching for the approach of other soldiers. Their standing orders were always silence on any mission away from the stronghold. There also were three members of the "Riservarsi" perched high in the cliffs above armed to the teeth, and their youthful eyes scanning the area for Nazi Scouts, or the Carabinieri.

He proclaimed loudly to his Paisons that what he was about to do was "alla Vecchia Maniera," "the old ways" as he sat in front of and in full view of these men slowly honing a ten-inch curved butcher knife on a stone. He slowly slid the blade which was lubricated in pepper oil first one way on the blood red whetstone, flipped it over and slid it the other way, all the while dividing his attention with this skilled task and the eyes of the man that had called him a "Jew lover" and spit in his face. There was a distinct smirk on the face of Don Biagateao, and he would cut side eyes to the other two bound men in front of him while the soft shinking sound of the blade continued. Don Biagateao's knife was already incredibly sharp, but he knew from the "alla Vecchia Maniera" that it was most important to show condemned men the implements that would be used on them first before actually using it. He also knew it was important to keep them alive as long as possible, and not let them lose consciousness from blood loss or the freezing cold.

All of the area they occupied that day on Monte Cuccio and in those moments was quiet and unusually warm for January. This was the southwestern side of a hill, and sheltered on two sides by a 80 foot sheer rocky wall. It was hidden from view by a vast series of chasms to their east, that lay as far as the eyes could see. Their escape route, should they need it would be via a natural limestone tunnel ¼ of a mile to the north. This tunnel led to a goat path many hundreds of meters below to their stronghold.

Don Biagateao took this time while sharpening his knife, to tell a story in his native tongue and then would use German to speak to his captives. He spoke in descriptive and colorful language, and used pauses to sip heated wine from a leather carafe.

"Thirty-two years ago , in a place like this in (northern mountain range in Italy) I sat with my grandfather, and your fathers," he said looking at the ligated Nazi's. "German soldiers came to our beautiful countryside then, only in ships," he recounted. "They, like you, looked down on us, and saw us as inferior to you. It was in a spot just like this one we turned many of the Germans into spiders with eight legs. Have you ever seen that?" he asked. " No? I didn't think so, and if you had you would not have come back here."

While he spoke one of the captured Germans, the captain, began to weep. This captain being the smartest of the captured soldiers knew exactly what he was speaking of. He wept very loudly knowing what fate would hold for him on Monte Cuccio. The major and the sergeant still believed that the Italians, especially this group were racially inferior bunglers and were only planning to scare them.

He invited all of his Paisons including the "Riservasi" to come closer to the men to see the look in their eyes, especially young Santo. Then he'd ask, which one was the bravest? Who was the weakest? What were they thinking? Was it death they feared or was it the method of death they feared?

Which one spoke the most, or the least and what were they saying?

It was a festive gathering and since they were in the safety of the mountainous cliffs he drank more wine and passed it around for this most important lesson. Don Biagateao was happy, and feeling slightly giddy while he explained, "Nutrire i maiali con i maiali."

"They needed a pen of pigs to feed pigs to pigs, but this will have to do."

Once the display of his knife sharpening was completed to his satisfaction Don Biagateao put on his rubber rain jacket and gleefully and joyfully went to work on the bound naked men beginning with "Le Zone Verita."

Santo would stay with this group for several years, right up until operation Husky which was the Allied invasion of Italy and the liberation of Democracy.

Italy was considered the soft underbelly in WWII Europe in 1943. The only way to gain control of the Mediterranean Sea was by breaking the Fascists and the Nazis' mighty grip on the entire Italian peninsula.

In July of 1943, the Allied forces began their massive invasion of Italy. The night it began the weather was ferocious, Sandy and his paisons had decreased their security and were for the most part just weathering the storm. It was at this exact time when four US paratroopers appeared from the darkness in front of their cave stronghold injured and severely disoriented.

Young Sandy was the first to make contact with them. With a form of broken English he explained to them using their maps and helped them get their bearings. They rendered first aid and a few moments by their warm fire.

Sandy and a few other boys led them down the goat paths and directed them toward other US troop locations.

In the morning light they witnessed thousands of Allied troops appearing past their stronghold and in the days that followed. This was like Christmas to Sandy and his paisons. They were the enemies of their enemies, or "Mal commune mezzo gaudio," a shared trouble is a half joy.

Santo left the safety of the cave with a group of American soldiers, and became to them a walking and talking road map and local guide. This is where and when he met Major Legatto, who spoke Italian. The two became inseparable.

With operation Husky in full swing and with maps drawn by young Santo, and their presentation to Major Legatto, it greatly assisted the rapid unraveling of Fascist occupation of Palermo and its surrounding countryside and ports.

These detailed maps were duplicated and passed up the chain of command by Major Legatto. Prior to this only the arduous and painstaking study of aerial photos had been relied upon for the Allied planning and advance.

The surrounding western Italian countryside had well over 50,000 Italian troops. The area was mountainous and extremely dangerous due to the places where pockets of resistance could hide and take up defensive positions. Obtaining control of the Mediterranean Sea was paramount for the eventual establishment of a base of operations toward the invasion of Germany.

While the Italians were no match for the US and Allied forces, several divisions of Group C of the Vermacht and the SS Elite Nazi troops continued to fight on once the Italians were defeated.

The City of Palermo and Sicily as a whole were extremely dangerous for many months. The bloody battles were from block to block and street to street in many cases.

As the Nazis were slowly pushed out, Major Legatto and his unit and with the help of the Cosa Nostra, restored water, electricity and provided food and medicine for the locals. Carpenters and stone masons emerged from other areas of the country and began rebuilding homes immediately.

Once the streets were safe and secure and the power restored, Legatto made the opening of all the bakeries in the city his first mission. He felt the smell of the baking bread would lift spirits and bring a sense of normalcy back to the region. He also had over one hundred thousand bottles of red wine shipped in and distributed to every street within the city, and saw to the reestablishment of the free press.

Legatto and his underground connections were praised and credited for saving thousands of lives. He received numerous citations and awards for making operation Husky a success in the collapse of Mussolini's regime.

Once full control of this area was established by the 7th Army, the British troops notwithstanding, Major Legatto was awarded the Legion of Merit, and the Silver Star for his role in making operation Husky a success and promoted to Colonel. He was now made the Provost Marshal of the entire city and went about establishing an interim military government along with The Allied Military Government for Occupied Territory, or AMGOT.

Again he found help from the underground resistance and Sandy and chief liaison Don Biagateao to this powerful group of partisans better known today as "The Mafia."

From the summer 1943 to the brutal winter of that year, Sandy as he was called and Legatto were practically insepara-ble. Legatto and his staff took great care of young Sandy, mak-ing sure he had warm clothes, hot food and a safe place to sleep at night. He was like an official mascot of the unit. Sandy and Major Legatto would sit long into the evenings and play chess .

Santo looked up to Abraham Legatto, not just his inter-esting English accented Italian, but his height. He had never seen anyone as tall as Legatto who stood six foot six. The way he walked and the way he commanded respect without being mean or violent. Mr. Legatto had this effect on just about any-one he met, but especially young Sandy who seemed to worship him, and grew to think of him as a father.

It was around this time when Legatto was notified that his sister's only son had been mortally wounded in Guadalca-nal serving with the US Marine Corps in the Pacific. He was a beautiful and engaging young man that had lied on his induc-tion form attesting that he wasn't an only child and he was 18, but at the time he was only 16.

With this terrible news and with the loss of so many chil-dren, Legatto went about making inquiries on how he could get young Sandy to the United States and away from what would remain war-torn Europe. Again it was the Mafia that put Legat-to in touch with Italian Catholic missionaries that could get him safely out of Italy and to the security of the United States. They did this by creating and establishing his next of kin that now lived in the United States.

As a tribute to Mr. Legatto, the boy's exodus to the US would cost him nothing, but the arrangement would have Don Biaga-teao placed within a key position of the new Italian government.

March 1st 1944, 13 year old Santo Salucci was put aboard a US Navy hospital ship and sent to Norfolk, Virginia. He was met promptly and lovingly by Reuben Russo and his young wife Mary who had only five years earlier escaped Mussolini's oppressive government in Sicily.

Now Sandy was a loving and integral part of the Russo family that resided as citizens in the United States of America.

SWEAT GLANDS

The day Kenny arrived from Michigan on his annual visit my mother would welcome him with a nice meal of his favorite foods. He wasn't much of an eater, but she knew he loved her spaghetti and she would affectionately prepare a pot the night before his arrival. She made the spaghetti the night before since it always seemed to taste better the next day. The day of his arrival she'd make a meat loaf, ribeye steaks and a Dutch apple pie. She also would go buy a pint of fresh vanilla ice cream from Carvel's. It was because of all of this cooking, that I knew Kenny was coming for the summer.

At the table that afternoon we all learned that eight year old Kenny had no manners at all.

He hadn't learned how to wash his hands before meals. He didn't know how to politely hold a knife or fork. He didn't know how to ask for food to be passed to him, instead he'd crane over the table and snatch a piece of steak off the platter, hunch over, then hurriedly eat it! This horrified my parents, who urgently began teaching him basic table etiquette.

The instant dinner was over, my mom would take all of his clothes and wash them and put him promptly in a soapy bathtub. Only my father knew she would quietly cry when she saw how filthy his socks and underwear were. The fetid smell of grimy underwear, and the acrid overpowering scent from his socks made her cringe into sadness.

She would vigorously scrub his skin with a soapy sponge, especially his neck, which invariably was black with dirt. She would cut and clean his fingernails which were long and packed with detritus.

The next day, once he was clean she would take him to our local barber to get his hair cut and then on to shop for new clothes. She methodically sorted through the clothes he arrived with deciding which would go in the trash, or which would serve as rags my father could use. But one way or another all the clothes he came with were not to be worn by him again.

Kenny didn't like being scrubbed the way my mother would scrub him. He'd cry, and verbally object to how it hurt. This never stopped my mother or even slowed her down one bit. But he loved having nice new clothes, especially the latest name brand tennis shoes, which would come after the scrubbing.

Always the next morning we all loaded into the car and headed downtown to the storefront business district. The first stop was the shoe store, then the barber shop, and finally the clothing store. I didn't take much interest in clothes, however Kenny loved name brand clothes. What stands out in my mind, was the shoe store.

The moment we walked into the shoe store the heady intoxicating smell of new leather, shoe polish and rubber all combined with myriad vivid colors of the tennis shoes uniformly arranged beneath bright display lights made Kenny more excited than she'd ever seen him. Clean and crisp new shirts hung throughout like fresh fruit and newly printed money from smooth wooden hangers induced a hypnotizing effect upon him.

Initially, I think my mother was prepared to buy him a simple pair of pro Keds like I wore but she had never seen her beloved nephew so thrilled. It wasn't long after we entered when Kenny spotted the Adidas rack, and he hurried over to it.

He began reciting which celebrity he had seen wearing which color or which style of shoe.

My mother and I sat watching Kenny's exuberance while choosing which pairs he wanted to try first .

In those days a sales associate would measure your feet, and only after this he'd go in the back and return with a shoe box. He made sure that you could see the brand name on the box, and he would slide the shoe onto your foot, then in an elaborate fashion lace them up, before asking you to walk around in them.

Kenny tried them on, and floated around the shoe store like he had been instantly transformed into a celebrity! He tried different gaits, all the while looking at his feet in the mirrors that were strategically located around the store.

There was no way I could have understood what or how Kenny was feeling back then. In my mind at the time, they were just tennis shoes, and this was just a shoe store. But I had never lived a life of destitution or straightened circumstances. I had never actually needed shoes, I had only wanted my choice of shoes.

My mother calmly asked, "Would you like these?" Kenny nodded his head yes.

While they were boxing the shoes up, Kenny saw tee shirts and warm up jackets with the Adidas logo on them, which he also just had to have. My mother made no objection whatsoever and bought him anything else he wanted that day, not to mention all that he needed. He needed socks, underwear and even deodorant.

I had overheard my parents having a discussion after the scrubbing. "Kenny had a sweat gland coming in under his arms and he needed deodorant," said my mom. My dad suggested that she buy, "Dial deodorant soap and Right Guard spray for Kenny's underarms."

61

On the other hand my father wasn't so indulgent with us. He once beat us both with his belt for throwing rocks at a milk bottle. Instead of the milk bottle we broke one of his bedroom windows. My father being the consummate Army Officer, told us before the beating, that if we had intended on throwing rocks, we'd have only needed his permission first, and he would have accepted the broken window as a secondary and unintentional target.

THE N WORD

The local Baptist church had its annual summer bus ride to the ocean, out in Montauk, New York. My mom was very busy with her career, my dad was away on a business trip, and Kenny and I as very young children of nine or ten, got on the bus and rode to the beach.

I had been to the ocean many times, and felt comfortable being there. Kenny and I didn't stay with the group but we wandered far down the beach a few hundred yards, and laid our blankets down. A few girls, Kim and Kate followed us down the beach, or better said followed Kenny.

The waves were ferocious that day, and the wind was blustering. After a few trips in and out of the water, Kenny and Kim went so far out in the ocean that Kate and I could barely see their heads. After an hour they returned, and Kenny explained they were standing on a sand bar. I asked Kate if she'd like to go out there with me. She soundly refused, citing her fear. So I ventured into the ocean alone, showing off that I could make it to the sand bar. I must have gotten only thirty feet from shore when a huge wave swept me off my feet, and the undertow pulled me out further. I was fighting and struggling against the current. It wasn't long before I grew tired and began to drown. Like some sort of divine intervention a hand appeared from nowhere and grabbed my arm, and pulled me to shore. It was Kenny, always looking out for me ! We never spoke about this event, he only said, "Dave, it looked like you needed a hand."

Later that summer at Devil's Lake, Kenny saved me again. Kate, Kim and some other boys were having chicken fights. Kate was on my back pushing and shoving her sister who was on the back of another boy. I stepped back and off into a 12 foot deep hole in the lake bed. Kate began choking me as we submerged. We both would have drowned, but again there was Kenny who seemed to come out of nowhere to save his little brother.

Another time he was home with us for the summer, when he was eight and I was a very young seven years old, we decided to walk north to the playground to watch the older kids play basketball. As we walked, one of our neighbors saw us from the opposite side of the street. She came out of her house in a fuchsia bathrobe, and some sort of pink plastic bag on her head and yelled:

"Get out of here you Fucking Niggers!"

While I didn't know what a nigger was, I could see her face twisting as she expressed those words; the hatred in her eyes and venom in her voice still resonates within my mind some fifty years later. We walked a bit faster while Kenny grabbed my hand. The woman, whom I can vividly remember was young, perhaps in her thirties walked quickly toward the curb and yelled almost the same thing again:

"Get out of here you Black Niggers!"

When we finally got to the playground, I asked Kenny what a *Nigger* was.

He explained to me that *we* were *niggers*. When I asked him how he knew that, he said his grandmother called him that all the time. I had never heard anything like that before. Certainly my parents would have told me if I was, or if we were *niggers* I reasoned.

We had stayed at the courts only a little while, when Kenny decided we should head back home, this time though we took a shortcut using a path and totally avoided that particular house.

Later that day after washing up for dinner, Kenny, my mom, dad and I had just begun eating when I asked my dad, *"Why didn't you tell me I was a Fucking Nigger?"*

My father leaped to his feet and dragged me into the garage by my collar. He had intended on beating me, when young Kenny and my mother intervened. Kenny and I reluctantly told them the story of what had happened, and within 15 minutes two state troopers were standing at our front door, as my parents filed a police report.

Back at the dinner table, my mother picked over her food, and my father smoked his cigar, which he seldom did inside the house. It was then that they both explained the race problem that existed in the country and no one was to call me, or refer to me as *nigger* ever again. My parents sought to shield me from all the ugliness of this country, and wanted to introduce it one lesson at a time as I got older. They certainly were unprepared for this.

At the dinner or breakfast table, they spelled a great deal. I never heard the words "White" or "Black" people, it was always W–H–I–T–E, or B–L–A–C–K.

That night before we went to sleep my father came into my room, where Kenny and I sat near the bed playing with a toy truck.

My father sat quietly on the bed next to us, looking on while he seemed to be choosing his words carefully before speaking.

"Look, boys, there are certain groups of citizens that have a disease or are sick in the mind. This disease makes them feel superior to the rest of us due to their particular genetic make-up, that being their skin color and texture of their hair, or color of their eyes. Because of this we must constantly fight with them to prove they are not superior, and we are not inferior." He went on to explain it was wrong to think that anyone is better than anyone else based upon appearances.

He kissed us both on the forehead, and headed back to the living room with my mother.

From that moment my parents learned from Kenny's own mouth that his grandmother called him *"Nigger"* and that was how he knew about it at eight years old.

After Helen left The Reverend with toddler Kenny in tow, she went to live with her mom in Sault Sainte Marie, Michigan. A year after that she bolted again, and left Kenny to be raised by her mother. We were never sure who Helen's mother was exactly, was she her mother or grandmother?

Kenny and Helen both referred to this woman as "Old Granny."

Old Granny owned and operated a motel. It wasn't just any motel, it was the main motel and hotspot for Sailors and Merchant Mariners coming up the St Mary's River. My father would drop hints at the dinner table that the motel was a clandestine border brothel, and my mother would quickly "shush" him from what I remember. At the age I was then, I had no idea what a brothel was, and they certainly never explained it to me.

THE PEARLY GATES

Just 13 months after the *"Nigger incident,"* Kenny's Old Granny suddenly died in the winter of 1973. After that he was sent to live with his father who by then was the pastor at the Methodist Church, and lived down the block in the once beautiful and formally well-kept church parsonage. This meant in 1974 Kenny lived close to me, and we spent all of our time together! During this time, it was rare to see Kenny without seeing me.

That summer while we were playing in the South Side Junk Yard, Uncle I.C. Guise appeared from a path in the woods and asked us both if we wanted to earn money. The Reverend I.C. Guise told us to find ten or twelve bricks that were scattered in the bushes around the junkyard. He told us to bring them home and wash them clean with soap and water. After they were clean he would give us cans of spray paint to paint them, and he would pay us each $5 per brick. After some quick math this was the best deal we had ever had.

We had a search contest, Kenny found eighteen bricks, and I found fourteen. We took hours cleaning and scrubbing them down, to present them to my uncle. He would examine each brick carefully, bounce it up and down in his hands, and say "keep washing."

He sent us back to keep cleaning them, and provided us with more lye soap. After a week of cleaning and after the skin peeled off my hands, he accepted them as clean.

The Reverend then gave us silver and gold paint and told us to carefully paint them.

We had so much fun with this project, I painted half my bricks silver, the other half gold and so did Kenny.

Once we were done and untrue to his word The Reverend gave us each $20 and bought us two soggy ice cream sandwiches. As little kids we didn't argue with him, we were happy to help him out.

The Reverend sold the bricks as gold and silver tickets to heaven. The silver bricks would get you into a high tier of heaven for $50 each. The gold bricks were $100 each and would guarantee that you or even a loved one or pet would be admitted into the highest heaven there was. He told the buyers, that once you got to heaven all you had to do was show Saint Peter the brick and "BOOM" you would be admitted to paradise.

He sold all the bricks in less than five days.

Later that summer instead of wandering around the neighborhood or going to the basketball courts, we played in the South Side junkyard.

The junkyard was closed and there were piles of old rusty hog iron, wiring harnesses, old and crashed dump trucks, and stacks and stacks of automobiles from the 1950s and the 1960s scattered around the sandy yard. There were farm tractors, semi-trucks with trailers, and even old gas pumps. One of the coolest things, there was an old ambulance and a huge red fire truck that sat right in the middle.

Kenny and I would sit in the truck and pretended we were driving it and racing to a fire.

Many of the vehicles were in good shape or at least seemed that way but had been flooded by the rising Matipan River during a storm.

Kenny had the idea of looking around to see if we could find a hot battery as he called it, and we could put that battery in the fire truck to make the siren run. We took a stripped wire and went from washed out car to washed out car seeing if we could get a spark or arc from grounding out the battery. One particular pick-up truck had a what seemed to be a new battery that was indeed still hot and held its charge. We took the battery out later that day with some of my dad's tools, and put that in the fire truck, and sure enough we had the siren and lights flashing!

Regardless of what we did in the old defunct South Side junkyard, when we got home my mother was waiting for us near the garage and wouldn't let us in the house. She said we were simply too dirty to come into the house. So we had to strip down to our underwear and put all our clothes in a bag, and she marched us both to the bathtub for a scrubbing! By then we were too big for her to scrub us, but she looked in from the doorway and would give instructions on where to wash. I would have to go first then after she cleaned the tub, she'd run fresh hot water for Kenny.

Days later in the junkyard we had spotted an old go-kart that had been in a crash that had caught our attention. Kenny and I removed it from a large trash pile and decided to drag it home with us to see if we could have some fun with it.

It was twisted up with no motor, but it had a brake and gas pedal with cables, a wide metal seat, and best of all a cool metal steering wheel. It took us a few days but we got the frame straightened, and used an old army blanket to recover the seat. We repaired the tires and with the leftover gold and silver spray paint from The Reverend's brick job we painted it. We took the tires off and with the money from the brick painting job we had them patched at the tire place. They were slicks, big and bold and only slightly dry rotted.

Kenny and I took turns pushing each other around in it, while we made engine noises. It was fun at first but I was unable to push Kenny as fast as he could push me, and soon he became bored with it. I told him I had seen a rotor tiller down at the junkyard and we could go take the engine off of it and have a proper go-kart if we got the engine to run.

Kenny loved this idea, and we took a few more of my father's tools down to the junkyard and removed a 7 horsepower Tecumseh engine off of it. My mother came in her car and we loaded it in the trunk and took it home.

Of course it didn't work, that was the beauty of it all back then. It was full of rusty water and completely seized up.

Later that night my mom drove us to Riverside public library, and we checked out a book on Small Engine repair. Kenny read that entire book in two hours while I looked at the pictures before we went to bed that night.

The next day the first thing we did after breakfast was to begin the disassembly of the engine. We took it all apart and lay the pieces all over the garage. My mom looked in on us a few times during the day, and had a million questions, all of which I couldn't answer, but Kenny seemed to know what he was talking about so that she understood. It didn't take much but we convinced my mom to help us buy a new piston and rings, and a few gaskets, a spark plug, and a few quarts of oil from the lawnmower repair shop out on county road 90 in Riverside. We rebuilt the engine in three days and with just one or two pulls from the starter rope it fired up. My mom was there to witness this, and she was simply astonished!

That night we mounted it on the go-kart but we were still without a chain.

With one more trip to the lawnmower shop, we had a brand new chain and two sprockets which we hooked up in less than an hour. And just like that we had a brand new go-kart with the fresh powerful 7 horsepower motor mounted on the back !

The seat was big enough for us to ride side by side, and we road that go-kart everywhere for the rest of the summer.

We would leave out early in the mornings with $2 for gas, and hit the trails. There was an old washed out dirt path above the Devil's Lake levy that we rode all the way down and back, and would take turns driving. The motor was so very fast and powerful, sometimes it was scary how fast we could drive it.

After a few hours of driving we would simply drive it to the gas station, get 40 cents in gas, two packs of peanut butter crackers and two cold orange sodas and we would be right back out riding!

We zoomed past the house where the racist lady with the pink bag on her head lived, we powered past the old South Side junkyard, we terrorized the basketball courts by doing burn-outs and doughnuts on the blacktop. We went all over the place in that thing all summer long!

To pay my mom back for the money for parts, Kenny and I would work on mowing the lawn, or trimming bushes, or any repairs needed or unneeded around the house. One of our other projects together was fixing my dad's riding lawnmower. I think my dad had planned on just buying a new one when he came from his work out of state, so he gave us the green light to take it apart.

It took a week or so, but when my dad returned, not only had we rebuilt the rear axle, starter, blades and belts, we had painted it and put some big knobby tires on it that we had found in the junkyard.

My father described what we had done in one word, "MAS-TERFUL!"

It was only after my mom had gotten wind of the "Heaven Brick scheme" that she secretly, without my dad knowing or anyone else for that matter, made an appointment with Attorney Abraham Legatto.

Initially she sought to find out more on how to be award-ed custody of her beloved nephew, but needed to know where Helen was, and how to contact her.

Mr. Legatto and his team went right to work that night skip tracing the whereabouts of Mrs. Helen Guise.

Only one week later, Legatto's secretary called to set up an appointment to explain the successful results of the search, and collect the $500 fee.

Not only did she discover where Helen was, but learned to her horror the abominable truth of Helen's new life.

NO PLACE LIKE HOME

The mighty Matipan River cut through the town of River-side like a slithering South American anaconda. Its wide and craggy steep banks were littered with what was left of a piecemeal bulkhead made of large granite rocks, brought in by the US Army Corps of Engineers decades ago.

The Matipan River was a tributary of The Great Taunton River which flowed through Horse Neck Bay before spilling into the mighty Atlantic.

By the time its waters got to the City of Riverside they were dark, muddy and sometimes very angry. However, through our neighborhood it seemed quiet and meandered through twists and turns of our section of town, serving as a barrier between the classes of stratified and mixed racial groups.

Living on the north side of its banks, you probably had both parents, and they both had jobs. Further north was Deer Park Avenue and Hudson Street which was called Pill Hill. This was an area exclusively for families of the professional people. There were physicians, and dentists that had their practices within their homes. I remember these fine homes very well! Their lawns were meticulously manicured, the streets and sidewalks were clean enough to eat off, and even the air smelled better up there!

The south side of The Matipan's banks was where predominantly black, brown and poor white families made their homes. I am not exactly sure why that was, but I know that the land was lower and more prone to flooding, thus it was sold or rented at a much lower cost. These homes were not grand at all. Normally they were in disrepair, with at least three cars in the yard of which only one ran, the other two would have dogs chained to them. If dogs were not chained to them, they would be up on blocks, and grass growing up around them. Broken mailboxes, cracked windows, and typically after a rainstorm the front and side of the lawns would be converted into small lakes with four feet of water surrounding them like a moat.

Just to the west was Devil's Lake, which was a mixed community. It was mainly white before a dip in the local economy caused it to become rundown, and prices dropped as did home ownership.

Devil's Lake area homes were also very prone to flooding, however the homes were built four to five feet off the ground. They had a complex series of flood mitigation built into the streets and sidewalks. Mostly they were built high and sloped down to a drainage system which kept the water from sitting too long, or rising too high.

However, now? Educated whites with money were slowly returning. Stuck in the middle of this grinding gentrification were black urban professionals. Somewhere along the way they built their own high school, which was called Lake Wood High.

Lake Wood High School was a small high school of 500 students. While they had a good baseball team some years, they focused more on the arts. Their marching and stage band was among the finest in the state for over fifteen years.

My parents lived in what was once the wetland junction between the north and south areas of town and that placed us right at the center of it all.

High floodwaters sometimes crept up on our back yard, but that's as far as the water ever went.

No matter where you lived north or south all the teens were sent to Riverside High.

NOT HIGH, BUT LOW

After the long hot summer of 1977 and in the midst of the Son of Sam killing spree, Kenny and I began at Riverside High as Freshmen. The school was massive and had at the time 1,200 students per class, or thereabouts.

By then Kenny had almost finished puberty and stood tall at six foot one inch. He was lean with wide shoulders and had developed a smooth baritone voice. I had not even begun puberty at this time.

We were in many of the same classes, which was nice, since we could sit close to each other. Kenny was a whiz in school! Algebra, Geometry and the sciences all came to him very naturally. Not only that, the teachers all seemed to love him. I don't know if it was his looks, his voice or his willingness to learn but whatever it was, high school came easy to him. Kenny would come right home, and began all his homework assignments without any delay. He wrote reports, studied math, and took time to explain much of it to me. In geometry he seemed to remember all the theorems and proofs, and even the small nuances the teacher only hinted upon as possible test questions.

He had a knack for all of these classes, and taught me what to look for and listen for in many of the classes. I sat right next to him as often as I was able, but somehow his experience was completely different than my own, it was as though I was asleep in class compared to his ability to pay attention and recall small details of the lessons. During class my mind wandered around the room as I gazed at many of the girls and their beauty or lack thereof. At times I noticed the girls I sat admiring, staring at Kenny and also not paying attention in class. Other times I found myself staring out the window and thought of where my father was or was he staring out the window of his office. During all my gazing the drone of the teacher's voice faded into the background of my mind while I hopelessly daydreamed of a day when I wouldn't have to be in school any longer, and I would be free to make my own schedules or have my own life somewhere far away. It was a wonderful and safe feeling to have Kenny in school with me, and I looked up to him a great deal no matter where we were or what we were doing.

But it was much more than that, if I had a class without him somewhere in the school I would get lost. In my defense the high school was massive, and if lost it could take 15 minutes to walk to find my assigned class. A few times I had given up the search and just sat in the lunchroom and waited or arrived to the next class early. I seemed to be extremely confused during the initial six months of high school. It should not go without saying that missing class and arriving late made a negative impact upon the teachers and my performance in high school in those days.

The first quarter's grade reports were published and sent home around Halloween of that year. There was a gulf between Kenny's grades and my own. Kenny had all A's, and I'm sure everyone is familiar with the comment section of the grade reports? Essentially they were ad hoc comments handwritten in the margins of the grade report card. A short editorial from the teacher directly to the parents.

"A PLEASURE IN CLASS" and "Best Student in the class!"
"A complete joy!"

These were the descriptions from Kenny's teachers. I on the other hand had only "C's" and a D in Gym Class.

The Comments about me were positively grim.

"David has some Potential"

"Missing and constantly late to class"

"Work needs drastic improvement"

And one that still stands out,

"Lights on, nobody home," from my English teacher.

To this day, I remain unable to explain how I had such poor grades my first year in high school, but whatever it was prompted my parents to meet with my Guidance Counselor.

The dreaded day eventually came and we met with the Guidance Counselor. What he said to my parents was horrific. Not sure why this was, but the Guidance Counselor had to continually tell us during the meeting how long he had been working in the field of education. He prefaced most of his horrible observations that day by stating, "In my 28 years of education," or "in my three decades of working in this field or "in all my years, my professional opinion is..."

He didn't beat around the bush but was blunt and to the point, he suggested that I had a learning disability. The instant he said this my mother began crying, and fumbling in her purse to find her hanky. He went on to state that my teachers just wanted the best for me, but perhaps I should be decelerated and put back into eighth grade or at the very least placed in special education. The points of evidence he presented were that instead of being in class I was found wandering around the halls, or even in the lunchroom. In addition, my current class standing was in the lowest tiers in English, Mathematics and History. The coup de grace in his argument was that there were students that couldn't speak English that had better grades than I did in English and I was dead last in my class of 1,458 students. He explained that I had been pushed through school and the junior high should have held me there another year or possibly two.

My mother went from quietly crying to a full-blown version of it; meanwhile, my father began getting angry. The Guidance

Counselor kept saying this all wasn't punitive but for my own best interest, while my mother began crying inconsolably. "No action will be taken at this point, but for now a medical exam should be scheduled for David," was his last sentence before the meeting was over. My father didn't speak much after this, and my mother eventually stopped crying. We took my father to the airport, he kissed my head and asked me to try to do better in school, and he said he was confident of my abilities. He kissed my mother and then he was gone, back to his job out of state.

Later, my uncle sat at our breakfast table and bragged about his son's performance in school. This was no ordinary boasting, but he would cite Bible verses that somehow linked his work in church with his son's performance. Then he would say that my mother wasn't living right and that was why my grades were so bad, which had her in tears. Of course my father wasn't there for all of this, but I was.

I spent the next few days at an audiologist lifting my hands left or right when I heard or if I heard a tone or tones. Then it was on to the eye doctor to have my eyes examined with a slit lamp, and eye charts.

Not long after all of this my mother took me to our local medical doctor for a full evaluation and examination. After a full day of being poked and prodded I was sadly deemed "Healthy as a Horse." There was no medical reason why my grades were so poor, only that I had not entered puberty yet and there was no timed estimate from the medical community if or when it would happen. They then referred to a teen psychologist to have my head examined.

My mother's distant cousin Betsy referred us to her live in girlfriend who at the time was a counselor in her own practice.

Cousin Betsy, and how would I describe her? The first thing that comes to mind is that she insisted that I call her "Aunt Betsy" since she was almost my mother's age. As I got older I called her just Betsy and I referred to her as "Biz Bag Betsy" since she was always in everyone else's business but her own.

Betsy was tall, standing over 5 foot 11 inches. She was so-called fair skinned with a thick head of wooly black hair. When I began to pay attention to her I noticed she had a mustache of thick black on her that looked like a caterpillar was nestled asleep on the top of her upper lip. At least she wasn't the hugging and kissing sort of old lady. The inside scuttlebutt on Betsy was that she had graduated from Riverside high school in the top of her class before she left and was admitted to Brown University. There was never any debate about how smart she was, but she didn't finish Brown because of a nervous breakdown after discovering she was pregnant. Betsy left Riverside with her entire future and hopes and dreams but had to return home in 1954 pregnant and in those days disgraced. But as smart as she was, she managed to get married to another man while pregnant. His name was Martin, and according to my parents he was kind and loving to Betsy and their new daughter whom she named Lorraine. She had convinced Martin that Lorraine was three months early due to some sort of medical condition she had invented and he believed her. Betsy, Martin and Lorraine lived in the Devil's Lake area in a fine home, though Betsy was said to never have liked or respected Martin but he made her life back then respectable since she had a baby daughter. One cold winter the heat had gone out in their house, and Martin went downstairs to check the oil burner. While he was down there repairing it Betsy is said to have turned the burner to the furnace on, and Martin was instantly killed in the explosion.

Not long after that she met and fell in love with Doris Mc-Masters and they were the first openly lesbian couple any of us ever knew.

I will never forget this old woman who practiced "Family Counseling," at least that's what her shingle said: Dr. Doris Mc-Masters, Ph.D.

Dr. McMaster's office was in a small blue building at the end of County road 90 not far from the county jail and adjacent to the bail bondman's office in the town of Riverside.

My mother and I sat waiting in her reception area for only 10 minutes before she came to the door and called my name to come in. When my mother attempted to come in with me, she was abruptly stopped and told she wasn't permitted to come with me. My mom was not pleased with this, but she relented and thought that the doctor knew best.

Dr McMasters was a tall gaunt woman of 70 years old. She was dressed in an old-fashioned mauve pantsuit with a frizzled white saffron blouse. She sported the latest faux leather orthopedic walking shoes, with beige stockings. Her hair was a huge bird's nest of silver gray hair that was thickly piled on top of her large egg shaped head. Three white sticky tendrilled curls hung on both sides of her face. She had a red pen behind her ear, and a black pen sticking in her hair near her right ear, which appeared as General Motors racing stripes .

Dr. McMasters' inner office was covered in a dreary vinyl taupe colored wallpaper and well-worn brown wall to wall shag carpet, and it smelled of mothballs, stale mayonnaise and a hint of menthol cigarettes. Her small disheveled and severely unorganized desk faced the wall. The wall beside her desk was covered in diplomas and civic citations all framed and matching in dust covered varnished pine. A few books lay stacked upon the corner of her cluttered desk which appeared to be books she had written since I could see her youthful photo on their covers.

I sat quietly in a chair across from hers, in-between our chairs was a pine coffee table, also scattered with paperback books she had written. A few of which still stand out in my mind
   "Beating Masturbation"
   "A Teen's Guide to Sex over Sixty"
   "The Complete Atlas of Breast Feeding"
   "Euthanasia, Going out in Style"
   "A Woman's Guide to Circumcision, Do's and Don'ts"
Before I knew it Dr. McMasters swiveled around in her office chair and looked me straight in the eyes and asked me, " How long is your sentence and how many hours of counseling did the judge order for you?"

When I heard this I laughed slightly and before I could utter anything else she yelled, "This is no laughing matter, Mister Man! Your entire life is here in my hands right now!" she growled.

I began to try to explain that I didn't know any judges, and my parents had brought me in because of my grades.

"This is the game you wish to play with me, huh?"

She snatched the red pen from her gray bird's nest and angrily scribbled notes on the page, before she continued. She asked me of my drug use, and when was the last time I got high. When she asked this her eyes locked on to my own, burning a hole in the air between us.

I told her I didn't use drugs, but occasionally took a sip of beer when my parents had it in the fridge.

She curtly made a few more handwritten notes on the file's page before asking me, "How long have you been shoplifting and what was the first thing you stole?"

I told her I wasn't a shoplifter or hadn't stolen anything in my entire life.

She angrily scribbled on the page, and then said, "Mr. Rasp-mutin, unless you tell me the truth it will not bode well with you in court."

I told her my name wasn't Raspmutin, and I was here to evaluate why my grades were so poor. She looked at the file she was holding briefly before swiveling her chair around and grabbing another file.

She examined this for a few moments before she said "Ok, I see here you were caught masturbating in the girl's room and involved in a circle jerk."

"A What?" I exclaimed "I don't masturbate in school," I retorted as angrily as I was able.

It was then she got as red as a beet and as mean as a hornet before marching me out of her office, and telling my mother that I was uncooperative and she would be informing the judge of it. She asked us to leave and slammed her door.

Try as I may, I couldn't convince my mother that this doctor was completely crazy! She took the doctor's side, and told me that I would go back there once she spoke to Betsy.

A few days later and after my mom and Betsy had time to speak about my visit to her girlfriend's office, Betsy made another grand suggestion which was; "Take David to a hypnotist."

I must say that during all of this my father wasn't at home, and my mother seemed open to any and all ideas about helping me, even as bizarre as this one.

After school one day, off we went to the office of Thomas Turnberry, LH,PA on West Hudson Street on Pill Hill.

We arrived to a large two-story stone house that sat in the midst of adjacent stone homes in a section we call Brick Way. This home was surrounded by a 5 foot tall chain link fence, that had bright green ivy vines winding their way around it and they were in bloom which made it even more pleasant. We saw the shingle, and arrow that said "office around the side."

My mom and I walked into a brightly lit and well decorated reception area where a man came out of an inner door and warmly greeted my mother with a handshake and then shook my hand.

He offered us a seat and explained that today would just be an introduction and a get to know of the process which would only take 45 minutes, once my mom filled out all my information.

After all of that was done, he asked my mother to wait and he took me to another room, an inner office. By now my mother knew that she would have to wait without me.

Mr. Turnberry's inner office reminded me of our living room at home. There were two brown leather Broyer chairs, a large well bolstered couch, and end tables with lamps and a coffee table. One of the lamps was on but it wasn't very bright, or if it was bright the curtains were drawn, and only his desk light and some light that spilled in around the creases in the curtains. It was actually very comfortable, not too dark, not too bright. The office smelled of cherry pipe tobacco which was sweet and extremely fragrant.

He instructed me to sit wherever I wanted. I chose the Broyer chair while he came over and sat a comfortable distance away in his wooden desk chair that squeaked and moaned from his weight.

Mr. Turnberry was 60 years old and had a solid white beard, white mustache, and a full head of kinky white hair in a small afro. He was a large man with a beer drinker's belly, but he seemed very calm and kind. His voice was deep, and he spoke slowly in monotone.

I was nervous, but had convinced myself that I wouldn't laugh no matter how bizarre things were about to get, and I was relieved when I heard him tell my mom this was just an interview. However in the back of my mind, I imagined his waving a shiny watch in my face, or watching a pendulum of some sort.

He began with a few observations, one of which was that I must hate having to come here of all places, and how embarrassing it could be. I nodded my head while he spoke the normal spiel of confidentiality. I didn't believe him, not because he seemed insincere but due to all the different places my mom had already dragged me to.

He asked me about my physical examinations, which my mom had listed on the new client form. I mentioned what I had gone through at Dr. McMasters' office, and the eye and ear doctors just weeks prior. I also mentioned all the needles and pokes and prods I had at the regular doctor's office.

When I said this, he shook his head and seemed very understanding and empathetic with what was going on. It's difficult to explain, but I instantly liked him. He was warm, friendly and compassionate. He seemed to be most different than any other older person I had ever met.

He told me he suffered in school and didn't have good grades, and he explained the reason he had bad grades. He said looking back he didn't have bad grades at all, it was his sister that made he and his brother look bad since she was so gifted and smart.

He asked me why I thought my grades were bad, or what was it about school that bothered me. I can't remember what I said but I told him how large the school was and the sheer size of it made me uneasy. It was odd, because up to that exact moment I myself had not thought that an issue. Furthermore, no one had ever asked me such a direct question on how the school itself made me feel. In the past all the adults searched for clues, but had not asked me.

He calmly explained what I was feeling wasn't unusual and that large classes and large schools are very impersonal and that can make one feel anxious. He told me that today and in the days to come he would help me relax in school and relax in my classes.

When he said this and how he said it made me feel much better.

After we spoke awhile on what I had been through, he then gently veered to the point of my visit.

Then we went right into what he called an exercise. A relaxing exercise, which seemed odd to me since exercise was always the most non-relaxing thing.

He asked me to close my eyes while he read a paragraph from a book he had. It was a paragraph from The Old Man and the Sea by Hemmingway. After he read it he asked me to describe what he had read, and I did. He asked to imagine a waterway, a calm waterway, with no wake and only gentle waves and I was ensconced within a boat. That boat rocked gently to the current. Back and forth and up and down he said soothingly. Now he said, you are in school in the massive hallways in the safety of the boat, and nothing to worry about.

There was a ton of imagery he painted and I sat with my eyes closed as he continued this . The boat and hallways, the classrooms, and how safe and worry free I was.

Before I knew it he told me to open my eyes, and I did. When I did my mom was standing in the doorway smiling, and I had fallen fast asleep. It was the strangest and most relaxing of feelings that day, my appointment was over and I felt great!!!

Once we left the office my mother explained that she and my father just wanted the very best for me, and they would take me to the moon and back if it would help me in school. My mother was very sincere in the car that day. I told her I would try my very best to do better. But I was one report card away from being put back in to the eighth grade, or being placed in special education.

Meanwhile, Kenny continued to excel!

In Gym Class? Kenny's game was hockey!

He could skillfully skate backwards, then slide sideways to a stop while controlling the hockey puck.

In skating drill he was the first one off the line, he skated the length of the rink, circled around and was the first one back. Shooting and checking seemed to come naturally to him.

I could barely skate, and fell down a great deal. I was unable to shoot the puck well if at all, because the moment I lifted my stick I would fall.

At the pool?

Kenny could dive from the high board without any problem at all. I was afraid to even climb the ladder up to that board.

I couldn't swim with my face in the water but Kenny swam like a fish with his face in the water, and would turn his head every other stroke to take a breath flawlessly. His technique was commanding and artful. All I could do was dog paddle, which I had taken great pride in before seeing my cousin in the pool.

In the months that followed, Kenny had made both the varsity swim team, and the varsity hockey squad. It was extremely rare for a freshman to make any high school varsity teams, but Kenny achieved this feat without even really trying.

Coach Don Marietti took an instant liking to Kenny and his skills ! Kenny loved this praise from the Coach.

Coach Don Marietti was 6 feet tall, and had been a professional hockey player for a few years before a neck injury forced him out. Coach Don Marietti had a sudden flash in the pan with professional hockey in Canada for two months, before he was traded several times, he convinced someone somewhere he could teach and work with young people. He needed to make a living somehow, and while he didn't like kids, this would have to do, and he stuck around. Coach Don had immensely meaty and freakishly large blue veined hands that appeared as if he had hockey gloves on. He was forty years old and still in the prime of his life. He was also rude, obnoxious and lorded over the boys' gym center but he gave Kenny a free pass to come skate or go to the gym anytime he wanted. It was essentially a "get out of class for free card."

By the end of the second quarter Kenny had tested out of Applied Geometry after making A's on all the tests, and he didn't even need to take the final exam since he would get an A anyway. In Pre-calculus Kenny's grades soared on princely wings. This was a class I had failed, and was sent to remediation .

Kenny was in the top 1% of the freshman class out of the 1477 students. Because of this he was given a pass to go anywhere in the school at any time he felt like it. In December of that year he was nominated to be in the National Honor Society and some three Greek letter clubs of the High School. This was a true honor since they only inducted juniors normally, but it turned out that Kenny wasn't among the top 1% of all the freshman... he was the *number one* student in the class with a grade point average of a perfect 4.00! In fact, it was 4.19 and above perfect with perfect attendance. This fact combined with his physicality on the ice and in the pool made him loved in and out of class.

One class in particular stands out to this day as a life changer, and this was an electronics class. In it, we learned about switches, capacitors, and printed circuits. I had trouble, but Kenny loved and excelled in it, and pushed the teacher for more and more information about everything. Once he learned it, he explained it to me in a manner in which I could understand.

We ended up getting good grades in the class, I got a "D+" and Kenny got an "A +" which was par for the course.

He went on to take advanced electronics, which in part was offered by BOCES, which in the State of New York was the Board of Cooperative Educational Services. There he found a comprehensive class studying early computers, memory circuits and theory. This was all way over my head but again Kenny finished first in the class.

In the late fall of 1977 Evelyn Champagne King released her hit single "Shame."

I had been out with my father one evening and so happy that he was home and I was spending time with him. Since he was seldom home, he made it a point to visit his old friends. We went to visit one of his Lodge brothers in the Devil's Lake area. The Lodge brother's daughter was in the midst of having a catered party downstairs in their large ranch style home. I vividly remember that they had a DJ and when I wandered downstairs I heard "Shame" in hi fi for the first time, and it sounded unlike any version I had previously heard, the bass and the highs excited me and lured me further into the party. Looking at the turntables, and the lights, the amps and seeing and hearing the immense speakers fascinated me. I didn't just hear the music that evening, I felt it in my chest and my legs. There were pretty girls there that were at minimum seniors in high school but probably freshman at the local college. Standing there listening to this music and in the midst of the party, watching the DJ, I made up my mind right then, what I aspired to be ASAP. On the way home I told my dad that I was going to become a DJ after watching them control the party. He smiled and asked me to explain my plan to become a DJ, and he would support me in this effort. He went on to say that playing music is fun and exciting but to never lose sight of what I sought to be once school was over with, which was to go on to college. When he said this, he knew what my mom and I had been told about my intelligence and aptitude, but he was unswerving in believing in me and my abilities.

It wasn't long after this, when I presented an idea to my cousin. The idea was to build an amplifier with a mixer, and some speakers. If we could do this, we could play music and charge kids to listen and dance. Kenny loved this idea, and we began getting schematics from the school library and also the public library. During that time we checked out of the shop class some soldering irons, and borrowed other tools to begin our project.

On the weekends, and long into the night we worked on building the amplifiers and sound mixers so much so that Kenny didn't go home but stayed with us.

His dad hardly noticed Kenny's absence at night, but I think my mom would call him to tell him where Kenny was most nights, or just left a message on his recorder. Nevertheless, Mom would come into the basement and watch us work on this project while she asked questions, and we were happy she was interested. In the weeks that followed we had her drive us all over Riverside buying capacitors, switches, and transformers. Not to mention the wood and saws we needed to build the speakers, which she paid for.

Once we were completed we had a mixer that worked, an amplifier and two big speakers. Kenny borrowed two turntables from the local athletics store, who were huge fans of his hockey game playing skills.

Less than three months later with our homemade equipment, and borrowing some record albums from a local store we were ready to have our first dance in Spring 1978.

We asked Uncle Ivan to make posters and flyers for our dance party, using what was left of "Guise's Gawks" which he gladly agreed.

My mother was very happy to see all three of us working together, to see and hear the printing press working after all the time it had sat silently collecting dust in the basement.

We called it the, *"MAYDAY THROW DOWN"*

We had this dance at the church hall, with the express understanding that there'd be no alcohol or smoking, and it would end at 10 p.m.

Kenny and I decided to get a bottle or two of alcohol for the party, to loosen everyone up, and maybe to calm us both down. I was very nervous about this, and playing music in front of anyone other than Kenny was going to be very different. The Reverend I.C. Guise drove us to Feathers Beverage and Liquors in Horse Neck the Friday before the "MAYDAY THROW DOWN" to buy booze for us.

Feathers Beverage and Liquors was a beautiful place which sat on the main county road that went right to the beach. It had a large neon sign that hung on a metal stanchion that blinked and flickered in bright red "COLD BEER." Just below that another sign illuminated in blue neon said "Discount Beverages."

The moment we walked in, the cold sour smell of wet boxes and bottles caught my attention. Several large walk-in coolers hummed from behind massive display cases, and the doors made soothing swooshing sounds when they were opened and closed. Thick heavy insulated metal doors behind the coolers opened and closed with precise heavy clanks.

The wall-length glass refrigerated cases didn't have an empty spot anywhere within them. All sorts of beer, cold drinks and even cold fortified wines set within and were illuminated by bright green fluorescent lights.

A dark and imposing reinforced concrete loading dock sat one floor below, where big rigs made their deliveries. That too smelled of wet boxes, stale beer with a hint of rotten apples.

A freight elevator effortlessly brought heavy cases, kegs and barrels up and out with a noisy forklift. Two large Feathers Beverage and Liquors trucks sat in the back lot that were ornately painted with an Indian head that had three red feathers hanging from a leather headband, and one small panel van bearing the same name and logo.

The rest of the place was a liquor store with aisles of all the latest gins, vodkas, and whiskeys that sat on spotless glass shelves all within an arm's reach. There was a locked glass cabinet near the front register that contained the extreme high dollar wine and liqueur. Names like Johnny Walker Blue, Dom Perignon, high end cognac and champagnes.

As we walked up and down the aisles, we ran right into Ed Longbow, whose father Elijah Longbow owned the store. Ed worked there part-time. He and his dad lived only a few miles down the road on the Pasqotouk Indian Reservation.

THE MIGHTY

The Pasqotouk Nation had owned and occupied hundreds of miles in all directions of what was now ritzy Horse Neck and New Hampton Beach. From the Tousan Bay south to Devil's Lake north, the entire Matipan River and all the way to the Atlantic Ocean was once their land. However, now they were reduced and relegated to a small reservation of seven thousand acres or just over eleven square miles. The reservation was now worth a tremendous fortune in today's dollars. This reservation contained five pristine beaches, and many shorelines that bristled with aquatic life. The fifteen hundred feet high mountainous elevations called God's Breath could be seen from all beaches and miles out to sea.

These sacred hills had been usurped by the state and federal governments over the decades due to military flight glide path markers, and spotting towers during World War II.

Their population was once estimated to be over one hundred thousand and strong, but now they existed as only eight thousand tribal members. They had been pushed around, their land stolen and encroached upon and that it was still commonplace for interlopers to be found laying a foundation to build a home. These interlopers would have all the legal documents to prove they owned the land. In times past it would be a civil legal battle to overturn these intruders, but that remedy proved lengthy and expensive. The length and expense of those court battles were what caused the loss of the case and of their land. The tribal lawyers, at that time would simply run out of money to continue their fight in court, and the interlopers would win. This, however, was no longer the case.

The once docile and egalitarian tribe of fishermen, farmers and craftsmen had changed a great deal over the last 100 years. They were all now a no-nonsense nation of savvy business owners.

They were not only victims of land stealing, but every sort of crime that ever existed had been perpetrated against them. Poisoning of the water, rape, murder and kidnapping. Annually and since anyone could remember three to five and sometimes as many as nine of their young women would simply vanish. There would be no track or trace of those that had gone missing. And as I write this, young Native women going missing is one of the nation's greatest crimes, and largely goes unreported and barely ever investigated or reported by the media.

It was a grass roots radio station they had begun in a church basement which became very popular. With its popularity the tribe got its message out about the missing women, and it gained political significance. With this change it was awarded tens of millions of dollars by the state, and private donations. With this money they began to educate their people and build schools for Native studies, and pushed their 130 year old fight against the federal government to be recognized as a sovereign Indian nation. Once this was achieved they now had federal money and power to build infrastructure which included hotels, casinos and shops.

In the years after they were recognized as a sovereign nation, and with their building of their first casino and hotel, certain residents of Horse Neck, Riverside and New Hampton Beach boycotted and protested. The protest and ill will against them as an emergent financial power met resistance to the highest levels of local politics.

The local government had used every dirty trick in the book to stop them, or at least attempt to slow them down.

Property taxes rose exponentially, all the free parking was now, No Parking, toll plazas were set up, and loitering laws enforced. Three elderly tribal members were charged with jay walking and given 30 days in county jail. They even closed the main road toward the reservation 12 hours a day to slow business to the tribe's hotels and casinos. The tribe, responding to this pressure built two heliports, one atop their main casino, and another near the God's Breath Mountains. They built a ferry port to bring gamblers and shoppers in from nearby Newport by two large ocean-going ferries they purchased from Norway. The thinking was while the county and state could control the roads, the airspace and waterways were controlled by the federal government.

Ferries brought in food, booze, hotel supplies, and shoppers cheaper than by the roads it turned out.

This sparked an idea for fine dining with the amount of fresh seafood they could bring in. Another brilliant idea was setting up activities for children. While the adults were gambling, the children could be entertained at an amusement park. Thus, Pasqotouk theme park was born! Roller coasters, Ferris wheels, bumper cars, and go karts were designed and constructed.

They also began Pasqotouk wilderness adventures for hikers, climbers and horse riding enthusiasts. They were then met with racism from the local hospitals, and the medical community. This caused them to build their own forty bed hospital and medical center. They hired the very best doctors and nurses in the country. In addition to this the National Health Service was added to help with culturally appropriate staff and faculty .

All these new additions were advertised worldwide, and sold out very quickly.

The heliports and ferries transported gamblers and sightseers 24 hours a day, at a very reasonable price.

The nation also had become amazingly efficient at policing themselves and policing their own interests on or off the reservation. They had become a force to be reckoned with.

THE DRINKING AGE

E d Greeted me in Algonquin, "Naa-Ta –Haay Yaa."
     I returned the greeting, while Ed smiled lighting up the entire liquor store!

Kenny and the Reverend smiled at us both while looking perplexed at the same time as Ed and I had a conversation in this sacred tongue.

I had learned to speak this language from Ed's mom Holly Longbow, who had taught us both so long ago as children.

It was great to see Ed, and we told him what we had planned to do the next day.

"I can get anything you want," he said proudly while switching to English.

When I told him we didn't have much money, he just asked to get into the "MAYDAY THROW DOWN" for free. We agreed and told him the time and place, and he said he'd be there.

It was strange seeing Ed. I hadn't seen him in many years, and I had barely recognized him due to how grown up he now looked. It was clear that Ed was happy to see me too, which made me feel good, since we would have someone else there with us, and not just Kenny and I at the "MAYDAY THROW DOWN."

That Saturday, May 6th 1978 was the day our young lives would be changed forever!

Kenny and I arrived at the church hall just after lunch, and began setting up our homemade and borrowed equipment. We had speaker wires to run, plugs to find, tables to set up and chairs to move.

Ed Longbow soon arrived. We thought he would have brought a bottle or two, but he instead came with his dad's van full of cases of beer, and a case of vodka and gin with brand names we'd never even heard of. He also had cases of cigarettes, orange juice, plastic cups, a change drawer, a foldable bar complete with lights, an illuminated Feathers Beverage Liquor sign, and two steel blue Colt .38 caliber handguns. One gun was perched near his cash drawer the other was in a holster near his right shoe.

The three of us set up the bar, with all drinks being $1 including the cans of beer.

As things would go, some of our homemade components needed on the spot repairs which we discovered during the sound tests. This required a few trips to the local electronic store.

We got the music playing at 7 p.m., and opened the doors to the hall at 7:30. By 10:00 the bar was completely sold out of beer, and things were just ramping up to a full on party.

The first kids that arrived didn't dance, but stood at the wall and stared around, after first buying cans of beer from Ed. These were the only kids there for what seemed like hours. I got busy playing and mixing some of my favorite music, like the Evelyn champagne king cut, and mixing it with some other songs. To my amazement I looked up at some point and could no longer see the walls, nor could I even see the bar other than the dim lights of the Feathers Beverage and liquor sign. It was as if a bus pulled up and everyone came in at the exact same time. I didn't know when all the kids came in, but they were there and dancing. The music continued with my neophobic mixing, but they all continued dancing.

It wasn't until I saw the Feathers Liquor lights go out, which was a message from Ed Longbow that he was all sold out.

Once this occurred we opened the door for free admissions but played music the rest of the night.

It wasn't until 4 a.m. that we turned the lights on, and turned the music off.

We had charged $1 admission, and had made over $1,500 at the door. The bar cleared $3,500, which Ed Longbow reported to us the next day. He split the money with Kenny and me. We came out far ahead because we borrowed "everything" and we didn't pay the church for the hall.

Oh, and the Reverend Ivan Guise? He reported that we had closed promptly at 10 p.m., despite the fact we were still cleaning up empty beer bottles and cigarette butts on the church lawn when services began at 10 a.m. that Sunday morning.

My mother, who wasn't a prude, was nevertheless upset with me for staying out all night since I was only fourteen years old at the time. I explained I was with Kenny who was fifteen at the time, which she didn't buy. I then showed her the $2,000 I had made that night, she did a complete 180 and was no longer mad but completely astonished.

GREETINGS AND FELICITATIONS

Monday morning rolled around, and while in school I was asked again and again when we would be having another throw down!

Kenny used his share of the money for beer, cigarettes and new parts to build more audio components. I used my share to buy more vinyl records, new turntables, and proprietary speakers.

In the days that followed, I rode with Ed Longbow into New York City in the Feathers Beverage Liquors van. He had invited me along and mentioned he had to make a run to a place in the city for his dad, and while there we could shop for some real DJ musical equipment and not rely upon the homemade stuff. He was right, the homemade stuff was at best unreliable but it had gotten our foot in the door of the music business.

During our ninety minute drive into New York City, Ed and I had time to catch up on current events.

We began our trip speaking about the party and some of the gaffs and blunders of the night. We spoke mostly Algonquin and I had gotten very rusty at speaking it, especially when trying to explain how music is mixed or played. Ed caught me up on those words, and I committed them to memory.

Ed spoke to me like I was a member of the tribe, speaking to me about their intimate business deals and their struggles. This was a great honor to have him share this with me, and I hung on his every word.

Once we got into the City of Manhattan we circled around the block a few times at an establishment on East 125th Street. It was a brick storefront that simply said, "PAWN" on the sign out front. We drove down a narrow alley and arrived at an unmarked and well armored back door.

Ed honked the horn twice before we got out of the van. We stood silently in the alleyway for a few moments listening to the roar of the city, the taxicabs honking their horns, kids with their radios blasting. Finally, I heard locks being unlatched and an older man opened the door and beckoned us to come inside, before latching the doors. He greeted Ed in Algonquin and sure of himself that I wouldn't understand began speaking. "I have the complete list, but some of the items will take two more days, for 550 paracord please tell your father and.." Ed nodded his head before he quickly introduced me, and I spoke to the man in Algonquin. When I did his eyes lit up and he smiled and began laughing. We shook hands and he gave me a brief hug before calling me "little brother."

"Now right to business," he said as he pointed to five wooden crates stacked near the doorway that read "Rue Lafonte French Champagne" but with a shipping label written in what looked like scribbles.

Ed glanced at the boxes, nodded his head, and only then he asked about the DJ equipment.

The old man walked us to the front of the store, and there I saw professional music equipment similar to what I had seen at my first DJ party I had gone to at my father's Lodge brothers home.

I didn't know what we needed, but I knew how I wanted it to sound. I explained this to Ed's friend and he guided me wisely and some of the equipment wasn't pretty or fancy or new but it was durable, worked well and best of all priced to sell. There I bought four Boom Box speakers with brand names. And a good mixer, one power amp, used high end speaker wire, an equalizer and two microphones, and two beautiful brand new turntables and their needles which were now called head shells. I bought a hard shell case to carry the turntables in and the mixer. It was wood and covered in protective vinyl, along with wheels or casters for the speakers to roll instead of carry them. I was curious as to how all of this stuff was for sale and sat there on sale waiting for me, but it was.

I was able to buy so much equipment with $2,000 that it filled the entire van, and we had a few bucks left over. Once the incredibly heavy boxes of Champagne were loaded, all the musical equipment was put in behind and on top of them.

On the way back Ed explained the nation is fulfilling its destiny, which was to be on top, then to be despised, then to be on top again. He spoke of the sacred God's Breath Hills a great deal, and how they had been corrupted by outsiders, but now they are being used as the ancestors had planned, which was to be the key to spiritual enlightenment and a plague to the White Man.

The day flew past, and once we arrived home, Ed and I unloaded the van, putting the equipment into our basement. My mother came out of the house and helped carry some smaller things, and I think most of all she wished to see and speak to Ed. He was very kind and polite to my mother, and gently entertained her questions about his dad. She told him a story or two about his late mother Holly Longbow who was her dear friend.

Later that week at my home, I was approached by Coon Skin, the Bootleg Brothers, and Mule Train to become part of the new startup company which Kenny and I called Genie Productions. We called it Genie because it was going to make all of our teenage wishes come true.

The Bootleg Brothers were identical twins from the South Side. We all called them Bootleg due to their dark complexion, and their crazy bowed legs. Barry and Byron were gophers, and were very good at scrounging anything that we needed at the last minute; fuses, power strips, spare tires, or even gasoline. These two were a few years younger than me, and at 12 years old no one but their mom could tell them apart. I learned over time to tell them apart only by a glint in their eyes. Barry was a bit more outgoing than Byron, and was more of a scoundrel than his younger brother. Their claim to fame was at 11 years old they hotwired and stole an entire city bus from the bus barn in Riverside. The bus had been in the shop for repairs, so it was weeks before it was reported missing. The Bootleg brothers loaded the bus with friends and family and drove it down I-95 to Baltimore, Maryland for a family reunion. During the eight hour trip they stopped to pay tolls, buy fuel, and made a few repairs to it. Once the reunion was completed they left the bus abandoned in Dover, Delaware. This crime went unsolved, and there was no solid evidence to bring them to justice. Had there been, the Bootlegs were too young to be prosecuted.

Barry and Bryon Brown lived 12 doors down in a 4 bedroom house with their 9 brothers and sisters. Their mother's brother and an older aunt also lived in the home with them. They had five or six old cars in their front yard, a few of which were up on blocks and only one of which ran and was somewhat dependable. They were all extremely nice people despite their circumstances.

Mule Train had flunked so many grades that he had been placed in special education. What we initially liked about him was his incredible strength which was very useful in loading and offloading all of our new heavy equipment. I never saw him as mentally or physically challenged, though he was extremely fond of dogs, and would bring home strays he'd find roaming in the neighborhood. Several times before he was placed in special education he had taken a few dogs to school with him.

Mule Train's parents were not in the picture, and he was taken in by childless elderly Aunt Sadie who lived five doors south of us. She wasn't his actual aunt, we all called Sadie Waskins, "Aunt Sadie," or "Crazy Southside Sadie."

Aunt Sadie and her husband Mr. Ralph moved to Riverside from Jim Crow ravaged Tishomingo, Mississippi in 1950 in an effort to find a better life in the North.

Mr. Ralph found a good job at the New Port Shipyard soon after they arrived. He was hired as a full-time pipe connector refurbishing World War II ships. With this well-paying job they were able to buy a home, a new car and even had some savings, all of which they were unable to do in Tishomingo. Mr. Ralph's daily job included removing old asbestos from the inside of ships, run new pipes and electrical conduits and replace the necessary asbestos.

Five years later he got sick, and was unable to continue working at the shipyard.

Mr. Ralph, who was very ambitious fell back on a skill he had developed in Tishomingo, Mississippi, which was making moonshine. With his ability to bend and fashion pipes together, he went about converting his garage into a whiskey making operation.

He sold his delicious and smooth Tishomingo Sipping Whiskey, cognac and even homemade wines around Riverside and Devil's Lake area one or two mason jars at a time. He was very successful with this and for many years after developing asbestosis he and Aunt Sadie continued a good living.

The details are still very sketchy, but one summer night in 1972 while fishing for Pumpkinseed Bass on the Matipan River, Mr. Ralph fell out of his boat and subsequently drowned. Everyone in our small community was shocked by this event. He was loved and his friends and customers came out by the hundreds for his funeral. I remember this because my parents and I went to his funeral, and there must have been over seven hundred mourners at Albert's Funeral home that sad day.

The Scuttlebutt was that Ralph Waskins had a good life insurance policy for $20,000. However, the insurance company denied paying the policy since they claimed he missed a payment the month prior to his fishing accident.

As the years passed ,and relying only upon her savings Aunt Sadie realized she was broke and alone.

Since Sadie owned her home, she was told to adopt a child and "get paid," that's where Mule Train came into the picture. She went right to social services and filled out all the necessary paperwork. Social services did a quick inspection of her home, and not long after that 11 year old Mule Train arrived.

Mule Train's placement in her home was at first a windfall, and every month she received $303 to feed and clothe him. It wasn't long before she found it cost more than that to feed him, but he was such a sweet boy she didn't wish to lose him. She once had an inside connection to buy discounted food stamps which had helped her feed herself. But try and search as she may she could no longer find the young man that sold them.

With the incessant mourning of her husband and the worry of insufficient money eventually her health failed. Sadie began to experience confusion and black outs. The neighbors and even my parents said, "she went crazy." Sadie was eventually deemed Non Compos mentis by a local physician. Turns out it was merely uncontrolled blood sugar that made her "out of her mind."

Aunt Sadie went about having her diabetes prayed away.

She was sold a silver brick which worked for diabetes, high blood pressure and rheumatism. She was told to put the brick in a tub of warm water and then climb in with it and soak. She did this every night for two weeks. This caused Aunt Sadie to contract a horrible urinary tract infection and all her teeth got loose, and began to fall out.

Eventually, Aunt Sadie slipped into a diabetic coma and nearly died. When she awoke she found that her left leg had been amputated above the knee. It was young Mule Train that found her unresponsive in the bathtub after breaking down the door. He lifted her out of the tub, covered her with a warm blanket and dialed the ambulance. Mule Train saved Aunt Sadie's life and became a South Side hero!

Once her surgical site healed, she was referred to the local prosthetics laboratory to have a leg made. Due to a glitch in the processing they made mahogany complected Aunt Sadie a coral colored leg. She complained but they refused to remake it.

After that, part of her daily routine was to sit out on her front porch in an old flannel blue house dress and in a wooden rocking chair swilling homemade wine. She would sit and yell at passers-by and at traffic or kids on bikes or anyone until she passed out drunk. When Mule Train arrived home from school he would carry Aunt Sadie inside and put her to bed. He also learned how to check her blood sugar, and inject her insulin as needed.

Mule Train was a big kid and was over 350 pounds at the age of fifteen, and had eaten his aunt out of house and home.

To make ends meet, Aunt Sadie would bake cakes, pies, or mason jars of her homemade wine and sell them around town. She would have Mule Train deliver the baked goods. The crazy thing was that at times, when the pies or cakes arrived the customer would find some of the pie or cake eaten. When asked about the missing pieces, Mule Train would simply say that he got hungry on his way. This was a problem at first but they were in such desperate circumstances that our neighbors would buy them regardless.

James Robert Lee Vanorski, whom we all knew affectionately as "Coon Skin." Numerous psoriatic, or raised itchy dermatitis lesions covered his neck and scalp which made his skin patchy like a raccoon. Skin was short, stocky and built like a city fire hydrant. He had a head full of long light brown curly hair and piercing blue eyes. At nine years old, Skin had been in a dirt bike accident and lost one of his front teeth, which he never had replaced.

Coon Skin was at least two years older than me and had moved with his parents from some back woods county of West

Virginia. His family owned a single family house just to the south of the Matipan River. Coon Skin and his entire family spoke in a garbled version of hillbilly dialect, that they spoke very rapidly. This version of English was impossible to understand to the untrained ear.

His father Peter Dean Vanarski, had some sort of lung disorder from working in a coal mine while growing up and seemed always out of breath. Since there were no coal mines in our area, he took a job as a metal fabricator and welder for a shipping company in Newport. I don't think he ever wore a welding mask which caused him to have retinal damage, because he squinted and he blinked nonstop like he had soap in his eyes.

His mother Dottie May Vanarski was also very interesting, and stood out from the other poor white people in our neighborhood. She was considered a 4x4, four feet tall, four feet wide and wore her hair in a huge jet black beehive bun. Her beehive hairdo had a red rose painted on its center with some sort of spray hair dye. She was never seen without a cigarette and wearing lint covered black stretch pants. Her pants were always immodestly, shamelessly and obscenely pulled up tightly and form fitting into her thick crotch.

Despite all of this, and living in a so-called black neighborhood, his family didn't like black people at all. Quite often they referred to their neighbors as "Nigras" which was a combination of the words "nigger" and "negro." However, Skin didn't share this mindset with his family, and was always cool with all of us. Coon Skin loved black people, and didn't interact with any of the other whites in the neighborhood unless he had to.

Another thing I didn't understand was how he spoke to his mother and father. He called his father "Shit Face Pete" and his mother he called by her first name which was "Dottie May." He yelled and cursed at his parents all the time and never got in trouble for this behavior.

Skin loved music as much as we all did; in fact, he could read sheet music and played the guitar. Also, while he spoke in the most unintelligible version of English, his singing voice was as clear as a bell. He loved to sing, and sang all the time on demand.

What was interesting about my crew looking back on it now, is that we never paid them. They hung around us to get into the *throw downs* for free, get free beer, food, drinks and cigarettes. I did make sure that they all had new matching crew uniforms, which were blue sweat suits, and white on white Pumas. What was sure, in those days and at that age, was that teens wish more than anything to belong to a clique or group, so maybe that was better than money.

By the end of the summer vacation and me as a brand new fifteen year old the crew had two parties a month.

In fall of 1978 the movie, *"Saturday Night Fever"* with John Travolta had changed music forever, and we began life as sophomores in high school.

I had many new friends, mostly those in my crew and much to my mom's chagrin a girlfriend named Lucinda Luviano who was a long-term exchange student from Chile.

Lucinda was a small shapely girl, with a magnificent mane of thick black hair. She spoke with a thick Spanish accent and had a smile that lit up entire rooms. But more than that she was a tom-boy of sorts and had a hands on approach to life. She preferred wood shop to home economics, citing she had cooked all her life. I met her in English class where she had much better grades than I did, even though English was her second language. I invited her to one of our *Throw Downs*, and it turned out that she had a love for music. She fit into our group flawlessly, and she became my girlfriend in no time at all.

After school one beautiful fall afternoon, I came home to find a young man sitting on our front steps. I thought I remembered him from a few of the concerts of joy my uncle had at Devil's Lake . The young man I remembered was confined to a wheelchair, and I honestly thought this was his twin brother.

When I approached him he stood, shook my hand and told me he loved music and wanted to be a DJ. I was a bit dismissive at first until he began telling me who he was. He told me his name was Walt Wheeler, Wendy's younger brother. I stood shaking my head, still having no idea who he was.

I told him that Wendy's brother was a kid in a wheelchair, affectionately known as, "Meals On Wheels."

When I said that he lit up, and said, "Yes, sir, that's me!"

Walt Wheeler was a gaunt and shy 12 year old from the Devil's Lake area. One Friday afternoon he was riding his bike in front of the family home, when a pizza delivery truck ran him over.

He sustained a broken tibia, a shattered femur, dislocated ankle and worst of all a traumatic brain injury. His brain swelled and he remained clinging to life in a medically induced coma for two months. There were donation jars with his picture on them at all the gas stations and stores throughout town.

One day he just woke up and began speaking in a deep unrecognizable voice. The surgeries on his legs were all risky but he healed up in what was considered a series of miracles.

During this time he was in a wheelchair and was never seen without his Sister Wendy who pushed him around, and lovingly attended to all his needs. The local kids gave him the name, "Meals on Wheels" since it was a pizza truck that had run him over.

One day he stood up from the wheelchair and began walking, with a cane at first. Eventually he did away with the cane and walked normally. Not only that, he was selected for the baseball team for Lake Wood High School and played second base at the varsity level.

"Meals on Wheels" was a miracle kid! Before the accident he was gaunt and shy, now he was muscular and gregarious. Before the accident he wrote with his right hand, now he wrote with his left. He was all but unrecognizable to those of us who had not seen him in years.

While we stood speaking, his sister Wendy appeared from inside the house, where she had been speaking to my mother.

What can I say about Wendy? She was gorgeous with a body that would stop a freight train. Oh the train might not be able to stop, but it would back up just to have another look at her. She was a true and earnest beauty with a heart of gold!

Wendy's smooth olive skin shined like the morning sun. Her figure was crafted by the Creator himself into the most perfect hourglass shape one could imagine. At five foot seven inches tall, her hips flared at the perfect spot which was just below her tiny 20 inch waist line. Her thick light brown hair was shoulder length and had natural red highlighted tendrils that daintily framed her delicate face, and made her huge amber eyes glisten. Wendy spoke in low whispers, and it was difficult to hear what she was saying but she was warm, and in possession of a deep sincerity that dripped femininity. Her beautiful soul was further exemplified by caring for her injured brother in any way that she could, and she did so with great joy.

I didn't call him "Meals on Wheels," I just called him "Wheels" which he liked.

Wheels had a voice for the microphone, a radio voice that dripped charisma. He had skills in mixing music far above those I had painfully learned, and best of all Wheels was brave ! He jumped in anywhere on any beat to rap, or cut in any song with another flawlessly! He had a way of stopping the music and scratch the same beat, so that no one ever stopped dancing. He had an innate command of the crowds, and they did what he told them. What dance to do, what words to chant, or what sounds to make. I knew then that meeting "Wheels" was one of the best things that happened to me, and that he was just what we needed at the time, "our talent."

Wheels was like an open book, and he told me the best thing that ever happened to him was that pizza truck hitting him. I listened while he told me the painful story of his recovery and the years it took to learn to walk again. To my great surprise he mentioned a silver brick that his grandmother had found down near the lake, and after that discovery he always believed he would walk again.

He told me privately that when he turned twenty-one years old, he'd get over $1.7 million dollars from the pizza company so he was a millionaire in training as he put it.

While I had many new friends, I had also made a few enemies around school. There were a few other small DJ groups within school, from whom we took paying customers. We didn't play better music, at the time it was only our bar concession from Feathers Beverage and Liquor that drew the kids into our *throw downs*. Others were simple beefs over girls, or some disagreements concerning admission costs or just plain bullying. With Kenny nearby I had nothing to worry about.

BLACK AT THE PARSONAGE

Sadly, this was the exact time when Kenny decided and was permitted by his dad to drop out of school. When my mother got wind of this, she confronted my uncle on the steps of the church one Sunday morning.

A heated argument ensued and I remember my mother coming home crying and upset. She called my father and spoke to him at length about what Uncle Ivan had said to her about Kenny. My uncle cited that at sixteen years old Kenny was old enough to make his own life choices.

I was often asked why he dropped out of school. Kenny simply felt that school was a complete waste of time. I also thought it a waste of time, with my bad grades but I feared my parents enough to know that it was a bad idea if I had even entertained such a thought.

After not seeing him for a few weeks, I was worried about him and got off the bus after school at the church parsonage where he lived.

The parsonage had been the three-story jewel of Pill Hill on Hudson Street with its hand carved flying pillars and Doric columns. The inside was bright, airy and well decorated with New England's finest antiquities.

Prior to the Reverend I.C. Guise living there, the former pastor chose not to live there, so the church had rented it out. There was a long list of potential renters and applications carefully selected by committee. If you were fortunate enough to be granted a lease, you had it made in the shade. The views of the surrounding beaches, and the lake were easily seen from almost every window. Not only that, the church paid for all water, electric, cable, gas, and free firewood in the winter.

However, now?

All one had to do was open the front door, and one's nose would be instantly accosted by the vile smell of cat urine and dog feces.

This beautiful dwelling was now home to at least twelve cats, and three dogs. New trash was piled upon old from the front door to the back.

Hundreds of young, fleet footed and remarkably agile German cockroaches skittered from pile to pile. Leathery winged roaches ran up the walls, and scurried from kitchen drawers and cabinets. Dead roaches lay upside down on the stovetop and within the oven.

Two solid black kittens chased roaches around the kitchen in a sordid game of hide and seek , with the crunch of chitin carapace writhing bugs between their teeth.

The church members that had been assigned to clean and maintain it had walked off and refused to ever return from what they had seen there. The word "clutter" would not even come close to describing it, it was filthy with dirty dishes not just piled high in the sink but piled throughout the entire house.

Any clean plastic bowls were stained with a red film from the last meal that had been served in them. Besides that, anything clean had small black specks in it, which were cockroach droppings.

Pizza boxes sat on and beneath the couch, some of which had mold and plants growing from them. Litter boxes were overflowing and acrid. Ornate window dressings and priceless solid cherrywood arched doors had been torn to shreds by the cats or the dogs or both, and urine and feces were everywhere.

The second floor was where the reverend had his office, and sleeping quarters which stunk of body odor and unflushed toilets. Kenny had the third floor all to himself, and it also stunk and was in disarray.

I had never seen him so sad or angry, maybe the best word is despondent. He explained to me that his mom had forgotten his birthday, which fell on the first day of school. She didn't just forget but was completely missing, and she hadn't answered Kenny's calls, or any of his letters in which he had told her of the news of what a great summer he had with our new business.

Kenny cried into his hands, then got up yelling profanities at a picture of her that hung on the wall. I had only seen Kenny cry on the few occasions when my father beat us. I cried from fear of my father, but Kenny cried from embarrassment. It was not that his belt didn't hurt, but the beating was for doing something terribly wrong which embarrassed Kenny. This time, however, the pain that plagued him was from nothing he did, or didn't do, it was simply because he was alive.

I didn't know how to calm or soothe him, so I just told him I missed him in school and left.

What I didn't know and what was happening at the church parsonage, which my mother told me about only after I told her about Kenny not being in school, was that Uncle Ivan had been ministering as he called it, to young boys in his home in the evenings. Many of whom he had met while working in the men's jail in the years prior.

She went on to tell that she had confronted her only brother on his horrible behavior, and she was met by overt and belligerent anger! She told him he could do whatever he wanted, but he had a son to think of who was seeing all of his debauchery.

He stated that the "men" were always at least nineteen years old, which she knew for a fact wasn't true. While Kenny and I were having wishes come true at the parties a sort of hell was being created up at the church parsonage.

I am not sure why I asked my mom this, but I did. "Mom, does Aunt Helen hate Kenny because he's black?" I think it was the first time I had ever seen my mother speechless. Her eyes filled, she couldn't speak, but sat and wept.

"He needed love," is what she said, and kept saying.

She admitted Kenny never had the love of a mother, and she had begged Helen for years to let her raise Kenny. Her pleas fell on selfish and deaf ears.

She went on to say that Helen didn't like what Kenny represented in her life, which was an error. Her critical thinking had failed her, and when she discovered that Ivan was sexually involved with men during her pregnancy she wanted to abort the baby in the 24th week. It probably had nothing to do with her being white, and Kenny being brown. I didn't know what "abort" meant but it was clear that Kenny's mother lived in a completely different world than Kenny ever would.

The results of Mr. Legatto's investigation still privately resonated in Mom's heart, and she vowed to never speak of it to anyone. She had sworn this only after the meeting with Legatto to make her nephew's life the very best she could despite the circumstances.

That terrible day so many years ago, at the law office she discovered that Helen Guise's whereabouts had been discovered by one of Mr. Legatto's legal team. They found her living in Kootian, Idaho, and a member of the largest Neo Nazi organization in the United States.

She had remarried a founding member of this organization and had seven more children with him.

Mr. Legatto provided my mother with her address and presented photos of her with her new family.

When my mother heard this information she knew it had to have been a mistake, and an error. Even when Legatto offered proof in the form of recent family photos taken just weeks prior to the meeting she at first didn't recognize Helen in a Neo Nazi uniform holding a small child. She sat in stark disbelief staring at the photos trying to make sense of it all. She didn't completely understand it and asked Mr. Legatto what it all meant. He proceeded to explain what the group's ideology was and what they sought to do. When she heard this my mother began weeping. She cried so much so that Legatto rang for his secretary to bring her tissues and a glass of cold water.

She insisted that no one should know of this, and he assured her that no one would.

He kept his word, however his researcher was not bound by attorney client confidentiality.

On October 1, 1978, just two weeks after Muhammad Ali beat Leon Spinks in a hard won rematch, my parents had a small party to celebrate Kenny turning 16 years old. We had music, cake, and Kenny got money from some of the older people my parents had invited. What stands out in my mind is that my parents got Kenny a 1973 royal blue Oldsmobile two door convertible. It had a tan top and white interior, air conditioning and electric windows. It had to have been the best gift anyone had ever received, especially Kenny.

He was so happy to have a party! He was overjoyed in a manner I had never seen, and to be honored by adults became a source of great pride for him. I remember how he strutted around with his chest stuck out.

He was not to drive it until he got his driver's license. But that didn't stop us from at least taking it around the block to drive and sit in it. We did use some of our DJ money to wire it for sound with speakers and a high-end cassette tape player.

The Oldsmobile was huge and had a cavernous interior. The front bench seat could seat four people without too much trouble and the back seat was as big and comfortable as any couch I had ever sat upon. We spent endless hours just sitting in that car. It was only a month or two before Kenny got his license and after that we went everywhere.

CLASH OF CULTURES

October 9th of that same year, there was a terrible fire at the Indian Reservation School. This suspicious late night fire razed the buildings to the ground and claimed the lives of three janitors and one cook. This incident was being thoroughly investigated by the tribal law enforcement team.

As a result of the fire, Ed Longbow and two hundred and seven teenage Natives began attending Riverside High School. I had always gotten along with everyone at the Reservation which was really odd because they didn't like anyone outside their own group. In a greater surprise Ed Longbow was in most of my classes, and we had the same lunch, which in high school was not just for eating but socializing.

Ed's mom, Holly Westmoreland Longbow had been a school teacher at the Reservation Grade School when I was four or five years old. Holly and my mom had been good friends back in the day.

At the time my mom knew that Holly was home alone with a small son, and her husband was away in Vietnam. When my mom asked her if she would be willing to tutor me in English and reading for the summer, she agreed and I don't know if there was a financial agreement or not, but she came to our home four mornings a week to privately teach me.

I don't remember much about her, other than she was very pretty and she smelled good. For some reason I remembered the sound of her voice. We would sit at my father's desk, and she would read children's books with me. Those books also had written below the English, the written language of her tribe which was Algonquin so I inexorably learned that language too. She would bring Ed with her, and he would sit on the floor quietly and watch us, or read with us. This was my earliest memory of Ed Longbow, and perhaps why we became such close friends. There is however no masculine word in Algonquin for "Friend" so we called each other simply "Brother."

It wasn't many years after that, when Holly W. Longbow came down with bladder cancer and died.

My mom often, when I'd mention Ed's name, spoke in a wispy remembrance of how kind and sweet his mom had been. She had dedicated her life to education, then educating her son, and caring for her husband. Her husband, Ed's dad, however wasn't so nice. I think she just said he was "Crazy."

Mr. Elijah Jerimiah Longbow was a quiet man, and seldom if ever spoke. He expressed himself mostly with one word answers like "yep," "nope," and "hmm" along with nods, grunts, and occasionally a smile.

He like most of the men from his tribe in the late 1960s was drafted into the armed services and sent to Vietnam. Due to his extreme physicality he was put into the Marine Corps, and the day after his induction he was sent to Parris Island, South Carolina.

While there he excelled in Drill and Ceremony, hand to hand combat, marksmanship and land navigation. After ten weeks of basic training he was selected to become a sapper and Marine Corps scout, because of his natural ability to navigate through any terrain whether it was forests, swamps and even the jungle. At the time this was without question one of the most dangerous jobs within the armed services. He trained ten more weeks at Camp Pendleton, California, was promoted twice since his arrival, and sent to Vietnam as a brand new Lance Corporal. There he served with the 9th Marine Expeditionary Brigade as a squad leader. During his 13 months in Vietnam, Mr. EJ earned four bronze stars and numerous other unit citations, before coming home to his bride and young son who was already four years old. He was able to begin his own business via the GI Bill, and with this he sought a means to support his young family.

Mr. EJ Longbow owned and operated Feathers Beverage and Liquors for two decades and he had taken great pride in his display cases, and the building's inviting façade which was on the main highway, that led right to the beach.

His summer customers usually bought in bulk, paid in cash and were normally well to do professionals out for summer vacation.

Mr. EJ was a good father despite what my mother had told me. For many years after Ed was born, Mr. EJ would sit and speak to his son in the oral tradition as he had learned from his father Taka Tall Tree. It began the same way each night and finished in a different time in history. As Ed got older Mr. Longbow had to compete with the television or the ringing of the phone in the evenings, or school homework assignments.

He didn't speak to anyone outside the tribe at all, but he spoke to his son Ed a great deal. He taught Ed, loved him, and cherished his son, expressing it as kindness and discipline. Less than a year after his wife died, Mr. Longbow hired a Native woman from a North Dakota tribe to live with him and help raise Ed.

There had come a time when Mr. E J Longbow stood in line at our local bank as he did once every few days. An armed man came in and proceeded to rob it at gunpoint. As the armed bandit left the bank with the bag full of money, Mr. EJ Longbow grabbed the man, roughed him up and disarmed him single handedly. He then made the man lay on the floor until police arrived. When the police arrived they thought that Mr. Longbow was somehow in cahoots with the robber and placed him in handcuffs too. Mr. Longbow didn't resist or say a word. The bank officials and bank patrons explained what happened and Mr. Longbow was immediately released.

Mr. EJ became a local celebrity of sorts for a period of time. The local TV news station interviewed him, and the bank gave him a $50 gift certificate, a fruit basket and praised his bravery. When a reporter asked him on live television why he had intervened and disregarded his own personal safety, Mr. E.J. Longbow said in one of the longest sentences anyone who knew him had ever heard, "I messed him up because he cut me in line. If he wanted to rob the bank, he should have waited in line like the rest of us."

This wasn't the only time Mr. EJ had been in the news. There had been an earlier incident when two large men came into Feather's Beverage and Liquors one Saturday afternoon and proceeded to rob him at gunpoint.

One man pointed a large caliber handgun at Mr. EJ's chest and demanded all the money in his register. Mr. EJ opened the register calmly with the intent of giving the robber $10. One of the robbers leaped over the counter, pushed Mr. EJ to the floor and took out several thousand dollars after which they both ran to their getaway car. Mr. EJ followed them into his parking lot, but was now armed with his Browning 10 gauge shotgun. He proceeded to fire several rounds of buckshot into the fleeing car.

Nonplussed, he leaped into his van and gave chase for many hours. The robbers eventually ran out of gas, and after abandoning their car in the mountains of Pennsylvania fled into the woods.

Mr. EJ pursued them on foot long into the night before finding them both perched in a tree just before dawn the next day. After an exchange of gunfire, one robber was mortally wounded with buckshot, the other was beaten nearly to death by the boot heel of Mr. EJ, who had run out of shotgun shells.

The 31 year old Mr. EJ sustained a grazing bullet wound to his neck, two black eyes, lacerations to his face, a bite wound, sprained left knee and a spiral boxer's fracture to his left forearm.

Ed who was in the back of the store during this time, had alerted the police that the store had been robbed and that his father had been kidnapped by the two bandits.

This made the national media, not just because of the sensationalism of the event, but because the two men were escaped convicts wanted by the FBI for murder in what was described as a three state crime wave.

Mr. EJ received a federal reward of $10,000 for bringing these men to justice.

Because of this and his meritorious service in Vietnam, a senior member of the Tribal Government's law enforcement team commissioned Mr. E. J. Longbow to resurrect a long forgotten clandestine regulatory subgroup. This subgroup was called "Mitaaswi Animosh," or loosely translated "The Ten Dogs."

MITAASWI ANIMOSH

There isn't much known about this group of Native regulators. We don't know their identities, except that of Mr. E. J. Longbow. We don't know where they live, or where they train. We don't know if or how much they are paid, so the following is speculation.

Their expense account doesn't exist in writing in any ledgers anywhere in the tribal accountant's office. But it is thought it's well in the mid seven figures, and paid from mixed line items from every business the tribe controls, under miscellaneous expense. On paper they don't exist, and it's a tribal crime to even say the name Mitaaswi Animosh.

We do know that there are ten to twelve active members. They are all former military though it's not known if it's US military, Canadian or French. They are believed to be a special forces branch, trained in guerrilla warfare, and urban warfare—ambush, sabotage, hit and run and extremely mobile experts.

Their mission is to ensure the Pasqotouk would not lose another inch of land, and that the day to day business of the tribe runs without the threat of outside interference, which they do with extreme prejudice.

They were actively investigating new businesses which included but were not limited to the cause of the tribal school fire which claimed three lives, the seizure of their casino and dance club. They were tracking down $22,000 in booze stolen by police, and $95,000 stolen from a casino. Currently they were actively investigating a loan application which would put a lien on three acres of their beach land. They had several older cases that they were slowly clearing from their books which included the disappearances of three young women just a month prior to the school fire.

The bottom line with them was this: "They are in the killing business, and business was good."

They didn't kill all of those they had found standing in the way of the great Pasqotouk nation and its legitimate aspirations to survive, at times it was much worse than death.

After tracing two of their missing young women to an offshore sex trafficking scheme years earlier, they then had discovered to their shock its origins were perpetrated by one of their own tribal members. This 30 year old man had lured the two young women into a panel truck and delivered them to the Newport docks, from there they were taken to a so-called man camp near the border of Southwest Texas and Oklahoma.

Once they returned the girls safely to their homes they decided not to kill these rapists, but to permanently maim them. This maiming was carried out in a very unusual way.

Once the men had been subdued with 550 paracord and an ether-based rag shoved in their mouth, an ice pick was used to make a puncture of orbital bone just under their eyelids. This trans-orbital invasion was to scramble the front lobes of the brain, leaving the criminal alive but a docile blithering idiot. This was done leaving very little evidence and didn't bleed much at all. It was quick and painless. This spoke more loudly as a warning to the kidnappers than killing them, it was thought at the time. They did this to five men including their fellow tribal member who had sold the girls. The other members of the

119

man camp were snatched away from the camp and violently disposed of in a South Dakota landfill, all but one of them.

It's thought that they train in the winter in the God's Breath mountains, and in the summer train somewhere in South Dakota near the US Canadian border.

It is only my speculation that Mr. EJ has them operate as he did with the US Marine Corps in Vietnam with seven basic tenets.

1. Decide to be aggressive enough, quickly enough.

2. Have a plan, and have a back-up plan because the first one probably won't work.

3. Anyone worth shooting, is worth shooting twice.

4. Always cheat, always win, the only unfair fight is the one you lose.

5. Flank your adversary and always protect yours.

6. If you are not shooting you should be communicating.

7. Be courteous, be polite, but have a plan to kill anyone you meet.

THE FIX AND THE FAILURE

As dawn broke on May 1st 1979, there came the sudden and unexpected death of Mr. Abraham Legatto.

His obituary would say that he died peacefully in his sleep but anyone close to it knew better.

Abraham Legatto was born on July 4th 1893 in Montpelier, Vermont to Solomon and Tamar Legatto. He was the youngest of three children.

He attended Essex County high school and was the captain of the varsity baseball team, track team, debate team and president of the chess club.

He went on to matriculate at Tufts University and graduated Suma cum laude with a Bachelor of arts in drama and French literature in 1914 and was later inducted into Phi Beta Kappa.

Harvard Law school 1914 -1917

US Army WWII Service, Rank of Colonel, silver star, bronze star, Italian campaign. Legion of merit, order of the British empire, Military governor of Sicily, 61 years of Legal practice.

Sandy sat alone holding his small tin Saint Benedict's medallion that his mother had packed in his coat the night she was murdered and he fled for his life. The silver chain he added to it decades ago was wrapped in a loop around the palm of his hand.

The large extra-long bronze casket sat just in front of him, the aroma of a variety of flowers sent by his former clients, friends and associates draping the casket and most of the front of the funeral parlor.

Sandy was very sad to lose such a valuable member, a special and intimate member of his inner circle. He had never told the story of exactly how he met Legatto, but just a broad overview.

His mind shot to their business dealings together...

In 1955, the year Sandy graduated from Law school in Philadelphia he had a meeting with Mr. Legatto. He was given a plane ticket to the island of Cyprus and a certified check for $5 million US Dollars and $50,000 in cash.

His mission was to meet with the acting governor and contribute to the cause against the British occupation. The goal was to keep the heroin supply lines open through that country into Europe and the United States.

World War II had disrupted the heroin routes for many years, and the new route through Cyprus was wide open.

Sandy helped finance the Greek hostilities against the Turks, while Legatto financed the Turk aggression toward the Greeks. All the while keeping the heroin trade routes open through both countries and the Aegean seaports.

It was money and arms provided to both sides.

No matter the outcome, Legatto and his connections in Palermo with Don Biagateao would have a large control of the loan repayment through the natural resources of Turkey and Greece.

They would insist it was a loan, then if it couldn't be repaid, which it couldn't, they would simply wish to have certain licenses issued for mining. Also, certain ships to be allowed to leave port sailing toward the United States with iron ore and zinc from Greece. From Turkey instead of money repaid they would ask for copper, manganese or chromite mining licenses.

Another thing they owned a controlling interest in was local newspapers. With this they could continue, through propaganda the unrest between these two countries after the war.

They continued the unrest between the two countries while financing each side of the tensions with US dollars, and in return they had vast amount of heroin pass through their ports directly to Pittsburgh, while at the same time becoming captains of industry with cheap raw materials from the source countries.

These and other international crimes were for the most part completely legal at the time.

Mr. Abraham Legatto's death was ruled by natural causes with one phone call to the coroner's office by Salucci.

While that was simple, he couldn't understand who could have murdered his lifetime friend.

Legatto was found with a grimy rag shoved in his mouth covered with ether-based engine starting fluid.

Like the death of any court officer, Salucci began to examine the cases Legatto had been working on, case by case he sat analyzing witness lists and complaints. He was very familiar with most of them, since he had been the behind the scenes lawyer, skip tracer, lead investigator, and "problem solver" for the Legatto law firm for decades. Nothing jumped out at him at all. For many months he wondered about this and it kept him up at night.

RED NIGGER

At first glance Ed looked like a Roman statue, standing well over 6 foot 4 inches at 16 years old. Smooth, warm, richly tanned skin covered Ed's flawless face. Silky straight black hair cut short on the sides and high on top of his head, with a natural undeviating part, which fell just above his left temple. His eyes were unsettlingly brown, and penetrating and sat deep within his skull. Ed was slightly pigeon toed, but took long smooth strides as he walked, and held his shoulders back and head up, as his father had taught him.

In gym class I saw Ed's physique for the first time. He had grown-man muscles with a broad chest and wide shoulders and a slim waist to boot. The old folks often told Ed, and Mr. EJ how Ed was the spitting image of Taka "Tall Tree" Longbow.

I on the other hand was a late bloomer and at the time, still didn't have any hair under my arms, but I was getting taller.

He climbed the rope faster than any of us! He effortlessly lifted the entire stack of weights on the bench press. He didn't just lift it but was able to press it ten times! On the leg press? He could push the entire stack without much effort. Pushups and sit ups? Ed could do pushups and sit ups until our coach lost count.

What was most interesting was his temperament. In school he was unswervingly stolid, he never laughed or even smiled, and was prone to fight at the drop of a hat. In fact, most of the young men from the Reservation that were now at our school behaved in a similar manner. They had a beehive mentality, if you messed with one of them, you had messed with all of them. This mentality wasn't just for the students, it was for the teachers, or anyone else for that matter.

This new group accepted me in to it, because Ed and I were friends. I found this sense of inclusion to be like warm blankets on a cold night.

There was an incident in the boys' locker room when Coach Marietti asked me while Ed and I were changing clothes to go back to class.

"Hey, boy, did you take a shower?" he rudely asked me.

To that moment, I had never had any direct personal issues with him.

I told him that I had taken a shower. He then proceeded to manhandle me, pull up my shirt and put his large hairy hand on my back to feel if it was warm or wet. In the next instant he smacked me open handed in the face. I remember feeling as though a well-seasoned Christmas ham had been launched from a cannon and impacting on the side of my head. I saw stars, and went numb before I collapsed to my knees stunned! He yelled, "GODDAMN RED NIGGER LIAR!" and spit on me.

Ed Longbow charged the coach, tackling him to the floor.

The coach had some fighting skills, but he was no match for Ed. During the fight, Ed landed a sharp left to Coach Marietti's chin, which staggered him, he then began beating him with his fists.

Coach Don's meaty hand latched on and clutched Ed's throat. I thought for sure the fight would have been over, but Ed began punching Coach's arm until he released him. The coach who was now on his back was able to block a few of the punches, but Ed's immense strength prevailed. He beat the coach bloody! Once Ed was finished he calmly got to his feet and said, "Come on, Dave, let's go to class!"

He said this without any acknowledgment of what had just happened. I was still on wobbly legs, but walked it off and we made it to class and never spoke of it again.

Ed and I never went back to gym class after that, but skipped out and went to the lunchroom. Subsequently, Ed and I both got an A in gym class the rest of our time at Riverside High School without having to do anything. This was my first A in high school, which made my parents happy, that I was doing much better in school.

All the time I had known Ed Longbow before that, I had never seen him fight, or even be angry. Around me, away from school he smiled, laughed, was light-hearted and affable. He spoke to me in Algonquin, frequently if not all the time.

During lunch period when I sat with Lucinda, one or more members of the tribe would sit with us. In those times we spoke only Algonquin which I understood perfectly.

There was trouble almost immediately when the white students heard us speaking this language. I found it wasn't just the other students but also the faculty and staff of the school. The teachers organized a committee to forbid anything but English to be spoken in the school.

Once the tribal lawyers discovered this, they launched a federal lawsuit against the school district over this policy. Their argument was that French, Spanish and German was spoken and taught at the school so what was the problem with Algonquin? From what I remember this argument raged in the courts for several years.

Speaking Algonquin connected them in the deepest of ways. It made them all family, and it was a direct connection to the distant past. Just to hear it spoken was like hearing a new baby cry for the first time, or sitting with an old wise grandfather that had been long dead. It embraced the past and connected the present. For me as an outsider I began to learn that it wasn't just a novel language, but a type of religion that one held sacrosanct. When they heard me speak, or interject in this sacred tongue I was part of them, and they were part of me. Anyone who has ever gone to high school knows how important it is to feel part of something. To be included in a group is one of the highest achievements at that age.

In the hallways between classes we'd always stop and speak. There were forty or fifty teenage girls from the tribe there too. Several Juniors and a few Seniors that were so amazingly beautiful and womanly that the boys in school could only stop and leer at them, which happened frequently.

But in my case they came toward me smiling and greeting me in this sacred language. This I found to be one of the greatest gifts I was given during these times.

LOVE LESSONS

The summer of 1979, Michael Jackson had just released his first solo album "Off The Wall" the day before I was to turn sixteen years old. We all had spent the entire day scouring New York City trying to buy two copies of it, but it was all sold out. However, the Bootleg Brothers were able to find five copies of it, and I knew better than ask them where they had found it. As payment we gave them two pair of matching white on white high top Puma's size 12. That evening Kenny came to pick me up in his Oldsmobile with the top down.

Kenny built the backseat and the trunk to connect via the armrest in the middle of the back seat, so simply lifting the armrest gave him access to the trunk. He had a cooler right under that armrest, full of ice and cold beer, and that particular night he had added Boone's Farm Country Quencher wine, and a small bottle of Southern Comfort.

We drove to the ballpark two towns over in East Island and sat watching the baseball game and sipping our ice cold beers. We'd only been there for about thirty minutes when two shapely young women walked up to the car, Meredith Caryson and Summer LaFountre whom we knew from school. They were both cheerleaders, from Deer Park Avenue. This meant that their parents had money! That night they were dressed in stylish denim shorts and soft sheer cotton crop tops.

Right off the bat Kenny told me and Summer to get into the back seat while he stayed up front with Meredith. The top was down exposing the warm starry night sky.

In those days it wasn't good for white girls to be seen with us, so once they got in we immediately drove away.

We found a gravel road that connected through the woods to a small clearing. We parked on the southern side of Albert's Cemetery, which was over two miles from its main entrance, and safe from the cops or traffic. It was dark and secluded, but not overly so. The well illuminated southeast corner of Riverside High School was clearly visible less than two hundred yards away. The Little League Park's main field was just one hundred yards away and closed for the evening, but the lights were still ablaze. This was a very secret and private lover's lane.

The girls asked for wine, which of course we had, while Kenny and I continued with our Molson's Ale.

The girls had to use the restroom, so we all simply went into the bushes to pee.

"Dave, Summer is for you and Meredith is for me," Kenny told me. Then he told me he and Meredith would take a walk and I was to have sex with Summer .

Up to that point I had not had sex before, I had kissed Lucinda but never had gone all the way. Kenny explained to me what to say, and how to say it. He then handed me two condoms and wished me a Happy Birthday smiling as wide and beautiful as he was! He had set the entire thing up, the wine, the girls, the Southern Comfort, all for my birthday.

At seventeen years old, Summer was extremely pretty with a flawless complexion and midback length blonde hair that was thick and stylish. Her big green eyes shined brighter than any star in the sky that night. She was incredibly shapely, with a perfect hourglass figure.

Summer was a cheerleader and she was considered a season girl. She never dated outside any of the varsity teams. If it was football season she dated the quarterback. If it was basketball season she dated the captain of the team.

In school she never even glanced in my direction. As a senior she belonged to the group of the highest tier of popularity, as was Meredith.

Kenny knew them from his time on the varsity swim team. They had seen him compete and after that never once missed a swim meet. They had also followed him while he played varsity hockey.

Kenny announced that he and Meredith were going to take a walk into the woods, like we had earlier planned.

I did exactly what he told me to do once they were gone.

"Tell Summer you have a small surprise for her, then hold up the bottle of Southern Comfort."

I did exactly what Kenny told me to do !

Once I produced the small bottle, she smiled and her eyes gleamed with appreciation.

We drank from the bottle and passed it back and forth only moments before we began kissing. We stopped kissing to drink more of the ice cold Southern Comfort, only to begin kissing again.

Her long, soft and fragrant hair covered both our faces while we kissed. She coquettishly swiped her hair behind her ear only after we stopped kissing to drink.

Up to that point I didn't know how to kiss, and my only experience had been with Lucinda.

Of course I didn't say anything to Summer about my inexperience, I kept my mouth shut. I only said what Kenny had instructed me to say. I pretended I had kissed one hundred girls prior to that. I more or less followed her lead and if she used her tongue a little, I would use mine likewise. This all went over very well, until she began to softly moan while we kissed.

We continued to sip the sweet liquor kissing deeply in alternating cycles. During this she whispered my name softly and looked deeply into my eyes revealing a delicacy that I could have never imagined.

Summer's eyes seemed to turn grey, while her neck and face began to radiantly beam just before she lovingly placed my hand on one of her exquisite breasts.

Being there with her that night, with the stars above us was one of the milestones of my life. Though it was over forty years ago I still hold it within my heart with endearing reverence.

That night I lost my virginity to Summer the cheerleader.

It wasn't long after this event, only days it seemed when my voice suddenly changed. I grew several inches taller, my groin and underarms bristled with hair. Not only that, my thinking became clearer and my grades dramatically improved. My mom never said anything about my body odor but two different brands of deodorant appeared in my bathroom, as well as a bar of orange Dial soap in my shower. I assumed this was for my newly emerging sweat glands. This was long overdue, and I was proud of my new smell.

I would never see Summer again privately, nor would she ever speak to me again, but the memory of that night is still something I cherish.

In addition to my first sexual experience, and the metabolic gifts provided by nature, my father gave me a 1965 Chevy van from the Army Surplus auction. He had new brakes, tires and wheel bearings installed, before running it through a car wash and presenting it to me on my birthday.

It was old with the three on the tree column shift, and the doghouse motor cover between the front seats. I loved it! Hereafter, it was called the Genie Love Van!

LIFE AND TIMES UNDERGROUND

Genie Productions continued to rent halls, and have "Throw Downs" through November of that year. We planned to have one event every other weekend up until Christmas; that was the plan anyway.

During the week we'd all meet at my home to practice, rehearse and test Kenny's equipment that he had time to work on since he was no longer in school. In the eight months since the first "Throw Down," the crew grew to include: Coon Skin, the Bootleg Brothers, Ed Longbow, Mule Train, Meals on Wheels, Wendy and Lucinda.

My mom was okay with us in the basement and we could play the music loud, since she was at work mostly during the day and my dad was also away at work.

Ed would come with a case of light beer from the liquor store, and Lucinda would bring a block of ice in a cooler from her host family that they had used for the beach.

With all the furniture in the basement, we arranged into a sort of clubhouse studio, complete with curtains, coffee tables, armchairs, two recliners, love seat, couch, a bagel oven and massive printing press. An eight foot folding table upon which sat the turntables and mixers. Stacks of plastic crates marked "Guise's Gawks" held all of the 12 inch albums. Below the table were Kenny's amplifiers also upon crates with box fans keeping everything cool. Kenny didn't like extension cords, so he crafted custom power strips and wired them into a conduit directly from my parents' main breaker box.

These practice sessions were mostly just social gatherings. I'd work on the turntables, and arrange beats together that I had thought of, to get the group's feeling on it or just replay some of the songs that had gone over well with the crowds in the past. Occasionally, I'd get a thumbs down with my music ideas from everyone except Lucinda, who seemed to think I was some sort of musical genius, and loved anything I played.

Ed and I would, during these jam sessions speak in Algonquin. Lucinda would listen and seemed to like listening to us, however I noticed that Kenny seemed to not like this conversation between us, which at the time I didn't think much about .

While I played certain songs, Kenny would adjust the equalizer and volumes, being sure to note how the song had been recorded and where his settings would be optimal. Some songs were louder than others, and if not checked, this could lead to failure of the power amplifiers or be at the threshold of pain to the human ear, and the crowds would all get headaches. He also monitored the temperature of the components, if too hot he'd turn on an old church fan we had. He had a box full of voltage meters, and decibel readers. They were no longer tools, he called them instruments.

I think these jam sessions were when we first saw Wheels' talent really emerge. He could disassemble a song and reconstruct it as something brand new while on the turntables or what were known as "The Wheels of Steel."

Wheels explained that it was all a form of Interpolation where he would change the pitch of a hit song, adding some other beats to it and make it his own.

His voice on the microphone was also genius! When speaking into the microphone he explained that a bar was a grouping of 4 beats, and he would work within 16 points to speak words that rhymed within it. But not any words, a story would emerge that rhymed.

At the time I'd never thought of music this way, in fact I knew nothing about music, only whether I liked it or not. Wheels seemed to know why anyone liked or disliked something in music. To be more clear, there were hit songs that had parts with as he put it "energy" and parts that were "whack." He would eliminate the whack parts, and just play the energy parts of all the latest hit songs. During this, he would tease the crowd with small segments of other hit songs. Watching him do this, was like watching a conductor lead an orchestra, while juggling dinner plates. Wheels had an artful finesse with the needle on the record and used his wrist in a quick flick to make the turntable go right back to speed, once he had stopped it. There was no lag or sound of lagging when he stopped and started it in mid song, but more than that the needle never bounced or skipped while he manipulated it. I was in complete awe watching and hearing him. He made it look easy. Speaking from experience and after months of trying to duplicate this in my alone time, I always had a record that skipped, and a sound from the turntables that made the music untunefully lag out of pitch.

After he was done playing this fusion of music, there would be records all over the place. In fifteen minutes he went through fifty albums or more. My only complaint was cleaning up after him. The fix was having the Bootleg Brothers on either side of him as he handed the records off and Coon Skin handing him the records from the milk crates.

Wendy assisted Kenny in anything. She sat and stared at him all evening, while the rest of us stared at her.

Kenny wasn't interested in even speaking to fine ass Wendy, which only increased her overtures.

Wendy began speaking to Lucinda about this, who spoke to me about it and we all spoke to my mother and eventually Kenny. No matter what we said he wasn't interested in her at all.

After I turned the music off, Coon Skin would stand up and tell jokes, most in the form of making fun of everyone. Coon Skin was a comic, and overwhelmingly funny! It wasn't just what he said, but how he said it. He would make fun of Ed Longbow and his muscles, or the Bootleg Brothers and their bow legs. He'd make fun of how long Lucinda's hair was, or how big her eyes were, stating, "Yo eyes so big yow can see inta tha future!"

Of course we would each try to form a comeback when Coon Skin said something about one of us. That comeback led to an exchange that became so funny, that we literally would spit out beer to keep from choking with laughter.

Once he became bored attacking us, he would attack our mothers. How stupid the Bootleg Brothers' Mama was, "Ta ha giv birf to two dicks at tha same time."

Mule Train's Aunt Sadie, "had a wooden leg with a real foot!"

He would mention the extra skin that Mule Train had on his head, saying, "Tha back o yo head lok like a pack of hot dogs."

Over time, Mule Train learned to give Coon Skin as good as he got. Mule Train made fun of Skin's mother a great deal, mostly her big hairdo, stating, "it was a hair Don't!" The tight pants she wore that were always pulled into her crotch? Mule Train would focus on this one aspect of Skin's Mamma for months and months non-stop! I can't remember all of it but it always ran something like this: " Yo mamma so stank when you was delivered *the* doctor had on the oxygen mask!" Before we could laugh, Mule Train would quickly say, "Yo mamma so stank she made Right Guard turn left and call for back up." His timing with these playful insults was impeccable.

Coon Skin would almost always continue by making fun of Mule Train's size, "Yo su fat yo baby pictures fall off tha wall." "Yo su fat yo fall off both sides of tha bed." "Yo su fat yo have ta wake up en sections." Mule Train would laugh, and hurl insults back at Coon Skin, saying, "*You so white, you gets sun burnt standing front of the Television.*" These playful insults would last until one of them got bored.

Mule once said that Ed Longbow looked like a "*Dick wit Arms!*" All Ed did was laugh, and was smart enough not to reply.

The only one that took it as a sour turn, was Kenny. No matter what anyone said to Kenny, he would get angry or mad. He was unable to take a joke or a playful quip. I didn't think much of it, but it was well known not to say anything about him, or his "Mama."

We would sit and make jokes the rest of the evening until it was time for everyone to go home. While we did this, Kenny sat quietly nursing a beer and staying just on the fringes of the laughter. The crew knew this about Kenny, but it never seemed to make them like him any less. They just saw him as very intense, a man who was unable to unwind and let his hair down. Unwilling or unable to look at his reflection in the youthful eyes of his closest friends.

Wendy would ask Coon Skin to play something for us on his guitar. His favorite artist was Marvin Gaye and though Coon Skin couldn't say the words "*Marvin Gaye*" he could sing just like him. His favorite song was *Distant Lover*. Once he began singing, even my mom would come downstairs to see him and hear him.

Mom would stand smiling and transfixed as his voice grew into a soft falsetto, soaring high to silky alto and dripped soulful passion. Coon Skin's embellishments, his inflections and intonation sounded just like Marvin Gaye. He also could sing all of Luther Vandross's ballads. Coon Skin's voice could soar to falsetto, or croon in alto or even the bass range with each one melting flawlessly into the next ! It was like a miracle to hear him and witness this gift he shared with us.

In the weeks that followed, Wendy had lost all interest in Kenny, and turned her attention to Coon Skin.

In 1979, Coon Skin and Wendy Wheeler began a secret tryst, mostly due to Skin being 19, and Wendy was only 16.

It wasn't overtly noticeable at first, but we all could feel the change in the energy between them. During the jam sessions, they would sit close to each other, and laugh together at unspoken things. When Skin would play his guitar and sing he'd stare into Wendy's eyes. Wendy seemed to glow from this sexual energy.

We were all cool with this, since we all liked Skin a great deal, even Meals on Wheels was fond of him. The obstacles in their way were they went to different high schools, and sadly their families.

We watched Skin slowly transform.

Wendy sat on the edge of the couch with her legs open, beside her sat a small wicker basket full of combs, brushes, sulfur hair grease and small red curlers.

Coon Skin would come in and greet us all before he would sit on the floor and slide the back of his neck between Wendy's legs. She began combing his hair gently, then making parts to expose his scalp. Once this was done, she would use her fingertips to lovingly apply sulfur grease to his scalp, then she continued to the next spot. Once she had greased his entire scalp she'd begin to braid his hair into cornrows.

Coon Skin's psoriasis went into remission with Wendy's tender loving care, and we never saw him scratching again.

Coon Skin looked very comfortable while we all tried our best not to stare. We could only imagine what his head must have felt like while nestled between her amazing legs, and just below her breasts. A week later she would take his braids out, then comb and style his hair thoughtfully. On many occasions she would grease his scalp lovingly then put the curlers in his hair. Once this was done and our music practice was complete, he would tell jokes, sing and play his guitar with a headful of colorful hair curlers.

Coon Skin's walk changed. He began walking with a sort of sideways limp, and leaned his head to one side or the other. Then, he would lean his head to the side before speaking. He ended all of his sentences with the phrase, "Ya naw whet I'm sayin."

Coon Skin's wardrobe which at the time consisted of rural plaids, ill-fitting denim jeans and dirty work boots changed. He slowly began wearing urban solid colors. His favorites included stylish Genie Production Adidas sweat suits in royal blue or guards red, Jordache jeans and leather white on white Pumas. Skin also was seldom seen without a blue kangol furgora hat, or a black bucket hat of the same brand.

Skin continued to transform into the coolest man in our crew!

He sold his old pick-up truck, and bought a burgundy 1974 Cadillac Coupe de Ville with spoke rims, a multiple toned horn, sunroof and TV antennas in the back.

Skin finally got his front tooth replaced with a solid gold cap, that had the dollar sign on it.

When I asked Skin how much the gold cap cost, he simply shrugged his shoulders, tilted his head to the side smiling and said: "Mi Hun gat tha, mon, git mi som, naa wat im sayin?"

No matter what Skin said, I always pretended I understood what he was saying, while I laughed.

Coon Skin was on the fast track to becoming one of our neighborhood's first men of leisure, and Wendy never left his side.

There were changes in the Bootleg Brothers, too. They both grew taller at the same rate, and it wasn't long before they showed up with a girlfriend or two, to enjoy our jam sessions.

They discovered that they could never be convicted of a crime, because it would be impossible to prove which one committed the crime. There would always be plausible deniability that the other Bootleg committed said offense. I don't think they got into major crimes, but small things like stealing tires, record albums, or a car or two.

For the most part they didn't speak very much, but listened to the music, and enjoyed the free beer and free clothes we supplied. I really liked them a great deal, and to this day I can't tell them apart other than that small glint in the older one's eyes.

Mule Train was growing at an alarming rate, and he would eat two or three sandwiches during our jam sessions along with a family sized bag of potato chips. I remember his laugh most of all and he laughed the loudest and longest of anyone at the jam sessions.

Most if not all of our new proprietary speakers, or amps, or even the crates of record albums were very heavy. Moving the equipment up from the basement , loading it into the van, then unloading it and setting it up, then playing the party took a tremendous amount of vigor. Not to mention taking it all apart and reloading it, taking it all home and then putting it all in the basement again took a lot of manpower and strength.

Though Ed Longbow was the most fit member of our crew, Mule Train was the strongest by far.

Typically, carrying a one hundred fifty-five pound "Boom Box" Subwoofer up the steps of the basement normally took two of us, at times three of us. There came a time when Mule Train took one "Boom Box" under his left arm, and then at the same time grabbed a second one under his right arm, and walked them up the twenty-two basement steps and put them both gently into the Genie Love van. He seemed to make light work of it, like he was carrying loaves of bread. The large milk crates that were full or ¾ full of 12 inch vinyl albums were also heavy. The most any of us carried was one at a time using both hands carting it up the steps. At times someone would carry two of these crates at once , I think Ed Longbow did this a great deal, since it saved time. We never encouraged this since an accident could cause injury or damage to the albums. Again. Mule Train picked up two crates on either side, and carried all four up the steps and into the van, which was astonishing.

Mack "Mule Train" Tanner was one of the best crew members we ever had! His laugh, his willingness to help, his love of music and of course his incredible strength made the rest of us look good without really trying.

Most of all we enjoyed being part of something, a group and the acceptances it offered no matter what our flaws, or race or socio-economic status.

Once everyone was gone, Lucinda and I would clean up. There would be sandwich crumbs, empty beer cans, cigarette butts, and Coon Skin's hair on the carpet. Lucinda ran the vacuum while I wiped off the chairs, and took out the trash.

After this we would turn off all the lights in the basement and privately listen to slow music while snuggled closely on the love seat. The only lights on were those of the stereo components which gently cast shadows on the walls with red and amber flickers. We danced to Barry White's, and other love songs. I didn't know how to slow dance then, and neither did she, but we both learned. Usually we would just hold each other and gently sway to the music. These were our tender moments of time together, alone without the roaring party-goers or the peering eyes of the crew.

My mother spent time with Kenny making sure he had enough to eat, and washing his clothes, and often she'd go and buy him clothes. She scolded him for dropping out of school, and he agreed to go to the local community college and finish with a college degree and his diploma. My mom loved this idea. She was like his actual mom in her love and caring for him. Sadly, I think this all was too late for him, but I could see how much he respected and loved her and my dad.

It wasn't too long after this, and during the spring we started getting calls to perform at a house party. I would like to say this was fun, but showing up to a place where we had no idea of the power supply available, or the size of the place, or how many people would be there was unnerving. This is when I would ask Kenny since he wasn't in school to go scout out the place and see if it was something we could do.

Not only did Kenny go, but he took his volt meters and took readings at each of the outlets in whatever room we were to set up, he also checked the fuse boxes and made sure they could be easily replaced. Then he sketched out the room, and presented it to me when I came home from school. Together we would both decide if we wanted to do it, and what equipment we would take.

If we decided to do it, I called and told the person how much we charged, and that the charge per hour was for the moment we began to load our van, travel to the spot, unload, set it up, play the music and then take it all down. We added to that price if we didn't wish to do it. Quite often the customer was willing to pay the fee even if it was outrageously priced. Once we arrived and before we offloaded anything I personally collected the entire amount before we began and then we would arrive like a small army. Ed in the liquor van, Kenny in his Oldsmobile, Coon Skin in his '74 Caddy, the rest of us in the Genie Love van with all the equipment.

We normally had everything set up and ready to play in 90 minutes, and we insisted on not having any party-goers in the room watching us with one exception, once Ed had his mobile bar ready then party-goers could purchase drinks before the music started. Ed sold drinks until he was sold out.

Most of these events went off without a hitch, and it was worth the effort with the fun factor and of course financially.

Kenny transformed his dismal bedroom at the parsonage into an electronics aficionado's wet dream. He had books, on top of books, that were long overdue from the library. He had schematics hanging on his walls. His desk was covered in heat sinks, soldering irons and every imaginable part. When one of our proprietary amps had blown, he took it apart and repaired it. Not only that but he said he had made it even better, which I didn't believe until I heard it.

His homemade amps performed even better than the store bought ones. Many of the places we played were humid, dusty and hot which caused the amps to overheat and blow, and one brand in particular even caught fire. Of course Kenny knew why, and he solved this dangerous glitch.

Unfortunately, though, he suffered with the lack of love from a missing mother and a father whose behavior transgressed all decency.

THE CLUB

Fall arrived again, and with it I was a junior in high school along with Lucinda and Ed Longbow. Along with being in school full-time, we still continued to take on new jobs with the crew.

Mr. Terry Lunette called the house and introduced himself as the manager at the Club Lemans. He said he had heard nothing but good things about me, and that he was in a bind. The problem he had was urgent, and he didn't wish to get into all the details telephonically, but would I drive there and meet with him as soon as possible. I agreed to meet with him after school the next day.

Club Lemans was a medium sized venue dance club that legally could hold 750 persons. It sat three miles down the road from Feathers Beverage and Liquors at the junction of the main highway that went to the swanky beaches, and the county road that meandered into the opulent town of Horse Neck. Club Lemans was not well known for dancing, it was well known for its adjacent casino. Casino Lemans had the ugliest brownish green carpet I had ever seen covered with gaming tables, roulette, blackjack, poker and two large craps tables. It was a windowless and featureless maze and only the staff knew their way around once they were inside of it, due to one side of it that looked exactly identical to all the other parts of it. The slot machines? I'm not exactly sure of the number of slot machines it had, but they lined the walls of the entire place, and even extended into the bathrooms of the casino. All the slot machines were wired together and a million dollar prize was given away at least once a year to some lucky gambler.

Club Lemans and Casino Lemans were secretly owned by the Pasqotouk Indian Nation.

I drove there alone right after school the next day, and arrived at the back door as I was instructed. A large man named Big Nick walked me inside and to a small room behind the bar where Mr. Lunette held a clipboard and seemed to be working on inventory.

He was a man of average height, in the prime of his life at 40 years old. His head was completely bald, and there was no way to tell if it had been shaved or whether he was bald due to age. However, his full and thick beard more than made up for his head being bald. He had a full head of hair on his face in the form of a massive brown, black and gray beard.

Terry Lunette was remarkably fit with wide shoulders, a thick wide neck, back, and slim waist. That day he was wearing a taupe silk Armani two-piece suit, and white cotton shirt with a magenta tie that hung in a loose Grantchester knot. The very instant he saw me, his face lit up and he warmly greeted me and thanked me several times for coming to meet with him so quickly. He offered me a seat, but upon looking for a chair, and not seeing one I sat on a wooden crate marked "Rue Lafonte fine Champagne." He seemed a bit distracted by my choice of seats and said, " Let's walk and talk, Davey," and I followed him to the bar.

He explained that they had a break in, and he suspected his former DJ of robbing the place, and taking many of the stereo components, speakers, tapes and albums.

He grabbed another clipboard that said "music" on the back in a red marker, and handed it to me. "This is what's supposed to be here," he said.

I glanced at the clipboard and it was a long list of audio components, and a longer list of 12 inch vinyl records. I stood skimming it while he studied my face as I silently read it.

After a few minutes, he said "Tell you what, Davey, let me show you."

Terry Lunette was upbeat, and gregarious with me like he had known me my entire life. The way he used my name and how often he used it made me feel like I was speaking to family. It was difficult for me not to like or trust Mr. Terry Lunette.

I was most relieved I didn't have to read any more of the list since the words on the page all seemed to run together, so I followed him.

We walked behind the bar to a pocket door which he unlocked, and slid open revealing a hidden metal staircase. We walked up the staircase as it wound around and around and finally arrived in a hallway. The hallway was thickly carpeted with whitewashed walls. We walked down this hallway before arriving at another door. He quickly unlocked that door and opened it revealing a large well equipped DJ booth.

What immediately struck me was the view. We were now 35 feet above the entire club. The entire dance floor, bar and even the bathrooms could be seen from this booth. Booth doesn't do it justice, it was more like a studio with couches, coffee table and chairs. To the anterior of the furniture was the control center for the entire club. I could see where the equipment had been, and there were loose, frayed, and cut wires sticking out all over like uncooked spaghetti.

"Can you see now, Davey?"

"Yes, your equipment is gone, or most of it."

"I hope you can help me."

I continued to look around at the missing system, and between out the glass windows and how far I was above the floor.

I glanced at the clipboard, and somehow it all began to make sense to me.

He stood at the doorway, which had once according to the list had a 12" JBL Studio monitor above, though now just a single clipped wire hung near its empty metal bracket.

Mr. Lunette reached up to touch the wire and briefly inspect it and point it out to me, and when he did his jacket spilled open for a brief second.

Within his jacket and under his left arm hung a small black Israeli-made machine gun. It was hung cleverly from a black nylon rig over his shoulders and across his wide powerful back. Its muzzle faced down to just above his belt line.

When I saw this, I didn't feel fear, instead and for some reason I just felt inquisitive, and that I should ask him about it, but resisted this urge. I had once opened my parents' bedside table in front of my father, and we both pretended I didn't see a 5-inch vibrator laying within is how best to describe how it all went down in those moments. I think he noticed my reaction, but we both pretended I didn't see it, and we continued to look around the booth.

Not only did he need a DJ, he needed all new components ready to play for the crowds they expected for the weekend. I explained that I couldn't give him a price on the equipment until I had Kenny come and take a look. He told me that he was in a pinch. He needed a DJ and the music equipment that weekend starting on Friday at 9 p.m. and playing until 4 a.m. on Saturday morning and then the same times on Saturday night and Sunday night.

If I could do this he would pay me $400 a night. I told him I had to ask my mother about this job and wasn't sure if I could, but I could still have Kenny come right over to quote the equipment price.

I was taken by its swanky interior and the three hundred foot bar which was made entirely from Michelin tire treads with one hundred red leather Porsche crest barstools. Behind the bar was a laterally transected Formula One LOTUS racecar complete with tires, engine and beautiful blue spoilers. Thousands of colorful high dollar bottles of booze sat upon frosted glass shelves just below the racecar.

The dance floor also had a Formula One racecar motif, with brand name signs including Porsche, Ferrari and even Mercedes–Benz. Just above the floor and attached to a ceiling trestle were authentic and working traffic lights painted yellow. These lights were surrounded by loose wires where large speakers had once hung.

Once I left the casino, I drove directly to pick up Kenny after explaining the job I had for him.

It took Kenny four days, and thirty hours of nonstop work to get the system working again, using all the components we had. He emptied our basement out of speaker wires, amplifiers, turntables, tape players and every other conceivable electronic.

On Friday, when I arrived at the club after school, the music was on, and it was playing like I could have never imagined. I went home and met up with my crew to load up the albums. I sat then with Lucinda in my bed room and we totaled up the bill for Mr. Lunette. It came to a staggering sum of $12,000 for time and materials. I told him I needed the money before we unloaded the albums and began playing.

He disappeared for fifteen minutes and came back with the money in cash. In 1980 this was a ton of money and proved too much to put in my pockets, so Lucinda quickly stuffed the bills into her bag.

My crew began unloading, while I drove home and gave the money to my mother. My mother was fearful that I had somehow come into the money illegally, but with a quick explanation I told her it was from the casino, and the job I had been offered. She then smiled and told me to be careful. I explained that I'd be home at dawn with Lucinda.

That night with four hundred and fifty club-goers we became a professional music company.

Songs like Donna Summer's *Hot Stuff,* and *Bad Girls* sounded better than anything I had ever heard anywhere. Kenny coordinated the light show with the music. I played the music, Kenny monitored the equipment, and Lucinda was by our side while we were locked away high above the crowd in the elaborate DJ booth. The rest of my crew sat on couches and stools that were within the booth, sipping free beer from the bar, not unlike our jam sessions.

The booth was the very nerve center of the club!

The booth had illuminated throw switches, sliding switches, breaker boxes, conduits, gauges, and meters which made it feel as complex as an airliner cockpit. It also contained a wall of vertical metal racks filled with power amplifiers, echo chambers, equalizers, feedback limiters, power filters, cassette tape players, a huge reel to reel player/recorder, light mixers, sound mixers, and studio speaker monitors. The rack behind us was covered with thousands of dance music 12 inch albums. We could control every light in the place, door lights, bar lights, dance floor lights and we even had an intercom system to ring any other club employee.

If we wanted food or drink we simply had to pick up the phone and they brought it right up to us. It felt like we were rock stars.

Ed Longbow and his dad supplied the booze for the entire place, which they kept double locked behind a steel door that said "Broom Closet."

Ed's job at the club was to make sure all beer and seltzer taps and everything at the bar worked during the night. It usually did, so he was able to hang with us in the DJ booth.

That Saturday night five hundred and twenty-five club-goers showed up to dance to our music.

What I understand now is that we were providing escapism. Escape from the racial tension that existed at the time. Also escape and freedom, though temporary from the terrible economy, gas shortages, taxes, inflation and unemployment that were also ravaging the country. To help them become totally immersed in the music and the dancing experience, with sound and lights. Marijuana and cocaine also were an accepted part of the club experience, though I didn't know anything about drugs or where they were obtained.

This was the very beginning of disco and an emerging culture, the club culture. What I didn't know at the time, was that drugs and drug abuse came hand in hand with this.

Mr. Lunette, whom I met with on Sunday evening showed up with more cash to pay us for our time, expressed his great pleasure on how it all sounded and how many compliments he had gotten on the new DJ and sound system, and that his boss was well pleased!

We wound up with that job every weekend for over a year, and oh what a year it was.

By late June of that year the attendance of the club exceeded eight hundred party-goers. Not only that but the number of gamblers almost doubled that summer.

The crowds consisted of adults or older teens from New York City, New Jersey or other parts of the country who were there to vacation at the local beaches. They came to gamble all evening and then dance all night.

It wasn't long before we added a foam cannon, fog machine and a wall of neon lights, all activated from our booth. This added a new intensity to the party-goer's experience. And with the increasing sound and lights, the party-goers became more odd.

In those days one remembers three piece suits and platform dance shoes, but in the club I saw that it was a costume party. Nude women with only body paint covering their breasts. Men were dressed in togas, and one time a woman brought a goat into the club .

There were certain songs that I mixed in, or introduced with fanfare which kicked off the night, normally around 11:30. The song which I liked, but the older crowd loved was a song called *MacArthur Park by* Donna Summer.

Kenny remotely turn off all the lights in the entire club, and then we flooded the dance floor with fog. The only lights on were the eerie lights from the red exit signs, and a few lights far in the distance from beneath the bar. Then via an echo chamber, "Wheels" on the microphone announced, "Ladies and Gentlemen, welcome to the hottest club on the East End! Let's get ready to leave the planet!" With ambient space music in the background, and mixing it right in, *It's Raining Men*, and with each thunder roll Kenny flashed on the bright ceiling neon lights. These bright lights would flash, piercing the abject darkness like lightning, traveling the length of the club. In these flashes we could see the crowd's reaction to being totally ensconced in thick odorless fog, which we had silently introduced to the dance floor, during the space music. From there we would mix in *Knock on Wood by* Amii Stewart, and again flash the lights with each mention of "thunder and lightning" in the song.

The crowd went wild, and the dance floor was packed with people shoulder to shoulder and back to back.

We would all look down at the floor to see if everyone was dancing, and better yet, how they were dancing. It became a common insider phrase to say, "Look at that Goat dancing!" Which was a reference to the lady that came in with the goat months ago.

During the night Coon Skin would imitate any unusual dancers, and mimic them to the point of making us all cry with laughter. Mule Train would soon get on board picking out dancers and making fun of them, or just making fun of Skin's comedy. I didn't think so, but Skin and Mule Train were on the job training and learning how to work all the controls and mix music just from watching us.

We kids were experiencing, with front row, center stage seats this new counterculture.

Working all night long was a new concept for me, and initially I was nervous about it, I did not know if I would get sleepy or have to lay down, or if anyone would even like the music we played. I found that none of this was true, though I did have to do my homework in the booth on Sunday nights, so during these times, we'd play the tape from the weekend before, and just called it *Rewind Sunday*.

But working all night did help add reflection to what one did throughout the day, or help influence plans for the next day. Also, the energy from the crowd was contagious and intoxicating. I'd have a very clear buzz once the night was over, which at the time I thought was listening to the loud music, but then the music wasn't that loud in our booth.

The biggest issues we were having was keeping the amps cool. It wasn't just the equipment; it was also us. It got to be over 100 degrees in that booth at night. The windows would also steam up and become foggy. Coon Skin said it was Mule Train's "Hot Ass Breath." Of course it wasn't, it was from body heat of all the dancers just below.

Once we addressed this issue to Mr. Lunette he had more fans and AC vents added to the booth. He also added more comfortable chairs for us to sit in and a small table for our meals. The weekends usually went by without any major hitches that Kenny could not quickly fix without any sound loss.

Mr. Lunette gave us money for more amps, more speakers, and whatever else we thought that we might need. The walls and ceiling were full of strobes, spots, pins and robot light assemblies. Kenny worked with four electricians to add power boxes throughout the club for more speakers and amplifiers.

Kenny stressed to us, that we were not trying to make the music louder, but making it fuller, which continued to show his brilliance. Kenny's idea about the speakers, were what I now can only explain as avant garde; he had them built into the walls, becoming virtually invisible and they became furnishings of the club. The speakers disappeared into the walls, floors and ceilings. There was powerful music on the dance floor, but 15 feet away at the bar, you could still have a conversation without yelling. It was a masterpiece in design and engineering.

With this huge investment the Club made a decision to separate the gambling section from the dance floor and erected glass walls and roped the doorways off.

A selection process of who could get into the club and who could not was instituted. If you were selected to enter you had to pay the cover charge which was $50 at the door.

The club became very exclusive after these changes.

I remember very clearly one night when I needed a cartridge for a turntable which we kept in the Genie Love Van and I was escorted to the parking lot by one of the security. I was surprised to witness a long line of over one hundred people extending from the front door, around the corner and then down the back alley who were patiently waiting to get in.

I saw and remember the fine automobiles in the parking lot. Brand name cars like Mercedes Benz, BMW, Porsche, Bentley and Rolls Royce. The parking lot was so full that some vehicles were parked on the sidewalk, or on the grass. These all signaled the wealth of the club-goers.

Endless notes were sent up from the floor with phone numbers and business cards from party-goers, both men and women wanting to meet me afterwards. Many were handwritten notes with song requests. Some of these request notes came with a bottle of booze, normally champagne, whether it was the house champagne or something high end. Other notes that I received during that time were Leman bar napkins written with lipstick with phone numbers and with the outline of women's lips after kissing the napkin. I found these the most interesting since they were in different colors of lipstick, red, fuchsia, pink and occasionally in oranges or even blue. But whatever came from the floor it was delivered at the booth door by one of the bartenders and given to Big Nick who stood or sat at the booth door, and following his strict instructions not to let anyone inside our booth. He would then hand the notes or the bottles to Lucinda who would put the bottles in a milk crate to be carried out at the end of the night, or the notes she put in her bag, and put them in my room once we got home. She was very cool about making sure I got or at least read every note, business card or napkin.

I seldom played any song requests. I had a list of songs in my head that mixed well together, in fact some songs were mixed together and the club-goers didn't know the song had changed since the beats were exactly the same. If I did happen to play the requested song, it was already planned in the rotation of songs.

There was so much champagne sent to the DJ booth that it became a chore to attend to it all. None of us drank champagne, oh we all had tried a few sips of the high end stuff the first few times it was sent up to us, but I ended up just taking it home with me and putting the bottles in the fridge for my parents. I can't imagine how my dad felt coming in the house after being away for three weeks at work, and discovering a $500 bottle of Champagne in the refrigerator. He wondered aloud if Mother had been perhaps entertaining while he was away? She'd simply say, "David brought it home from work." After a while there were bottles of expensive Scotch whiskey, Cognac, and wine in a kitchen cabinet just for them. These were the expensive bottles that Feathers Beverage and Liquors would keep under lock and key in their secure display cases, but they were now commonplace in my parents' kitchen. A few times I had accumulated so many bottles there remained no more room at my house so I sold them back to Feathers Beverage and Liquors; brands like Veuve Clicquo and Dom Perignon at pennies on the dollar. Mr. Longbow then turned around and sold the bottles back to the club. He seemed to be very happy to do this.

Cash and marijuana were sent up to the booth from the floor, and handed to Lucinda who stashed it away for me to examine later. The cash I kept, the marijuana I gave to whomever wanted it.

One particular night, I was handed a small envelope as I walked to the DJ booth. It was a $50 sack of high-end marijuana. I put this in my leather jacket, and forgot about it. After a long night at work, that Sunday morning I was sent on an errand by my mother to drop off a key to her Antique store to my Aunt Betsy. Betsy wasn't really my aunt, she was my cousin but since she was almost as old as my mother we called her Aunt Betsy. When I pulled the key out, the bag fell out too without me knowing.

Halfway home, I suddenly remembered the bag of weed and turned around to see if I had dropped it in Betsy's driveway.

I found Betsy in her doorway, and she asked me if I was missing something. She asked me if I was "ON THE MARIJUANA, and DID I need help getting clean?" She cited her girlfriend, "Dr. McMasters had already tried and failed to help me."

I told her how I obtained the marijuana, and she said she wouldn't tell my mother, but she was going to keep the bag. When I got home, I told my mom what had happened, and the conversation I had just had with Aunt Betsy.

My mom laughed and said that Betsy had already called her and told her. My mom being my Lawyer and Defense Attorney believed what I had told her, and let Betsy think what she wanted. I never knew what happened to that bag of weed, but I have a feeling that Betsy and Dr. McMasters rolled it up and smoked it.

Drugs were another part of the club life culture.

Drug use wasn't just in the club culture; its usage was exploding within Riverside High School as well. This wasn't well known at the time, but it became well known during that year.

KIDS' STUFF

I don't think anyone knew our ages back then, other than Terry Lunette who protected us by assigning Big Nick and Heavy Frank to keep our booth free from inebriated interlopers. I think our protectors also wanted to offer suggestions of music they wanted to hear. The music selection was left completely up to me or Wheels.

We also got other things for free.

I came home one day and there were two big boxes sitting near the door addressed to GENIE PRODUCTIONS. They contained free albums marked "promotional copy- not to be sold." These boxes really added up over the course of the year, and I listened to them in our group on Tuesday evening, deciding if I liked them or not. If I did, I worked the songs into playing the music on the weekend, or if I did not I just gave them to the Bootleg Brothers whom I suspected of selling them.

We all had new uniforms, mostly matching tee shirts, or sweat suits with our names on them, and our Logo "Genie Productions" on the back. We also all wore white on white Pumas during this time, which the club paid for. In fact, anything we needed or wanted we just had to ask Mr. Lunette, and it would appear. I remember asking him for a set of high end wine glasses for my parents' wedding anniversary. That Friday there they sat in the DJ booth.

I noticed many other students in school wearing white on white Pumas and Genie sweat suits, and when I asked them where they got it, they'd simply say Mule Train. We gave clothes to Mule Train who sold them at top dollar and then would get more from us for free after which he would go to the delicatessen to buy sandwiches. I strangely liked this about him.

With the new job, there were still calls for us to play at a house party or two on the weekends. I figured with some of the money we made we could buy more equipment, much of which was used and fixed up by Kenny. With the refurbished equipment we could bring Coon Skin in to DJ at the club while the rest of us could work at these house parties. Yes, Genie Productions could be in two places at once.

The money?

Well, I gave it all to my mom, every dime! With it she opened a trust fund for my Education, and she had a well-established budget where she gave Kenny and I both $150 a week. This was more than enough money in those days for anything.

Within six months she announced that there was enough money to pay for my first four years of college, and she was now opening an account for Kenny to go to college.

Those were wonderful days!

THE COMB

I arrived home from high school one afternoon to find my mom sitting at the kitchen table with a man she had gone to school with. I could see in her eyes that she was in mild shock, but covering it up. She introduced the man as Detective Underwood. He stood and shook my hand while he introduced himself as Detective Sergeant Colmazio Underwood of the Riverside Police Department.

As a kid I had learned manners and etiquette from my dad, so I squeezed his hand very firmly and looked him right in the eye.

He liked this, especially from a teenager.

"David, he would like to speak with you, ok?"

"Sure, Mom."

My mom excused herself from the conversation but only went into the next room where I was certain she was listening.

I'm not sure how I knew this at such an early age, but cops are known to ask questions to which they themselves already know the answers, so I knew I had to tell him the truth whatever he asked. I had no idea why he was there, but I soon found out.

Detective Sergeant Underwood, got right to the point and the conversation ran something like this:

"Have you bought any new equipment recently?"

"Yes, we have."

"How do you know that?"

"We run a legitimate music business, and we buy equipment all the time, and nowadays we buy it used."

"Why do you buy it used?"

"We buy it used and cheap, to rebuild it into something better," is exactly what I said .

"I'm looking for a," and at that moment he took a blue spiral notebook out of his jacket pocket. "Ahh, let me see," he said as he flipped pages. "Did you buy a Crown power amplifier SPA 2200?"

He looked up from his notebook to gauge my reaction.

Without any hesitation I said, "Yes sir, I bought one of those about a month ago."

"If you buy so much equipment how do you remember?"

"I remember that amplifier because it was like a tank and must weigh 100 pounds, like a ship anchor, and I couldn't lift it."

"Do you remember who you bought it from?"

"Yes, of course I do."

"What was his name?"

"I bought the amp from Henry Martinez, and gave him $200."

"You bought a $2,000 amplifier for $200? Didn't that seem odd to you, Davey?"

"At first it did, but it was in bad shape and it doesn't work, so I didn't make a big deal about it, since most likely it will be used for parts."

"He sold you a blown amp?"

"Yes, that's right, blown and banged up pretty badly."

"We'll need you to get the amp, and sign a form attesting who you bought it from. Will you agree to that?"

"Yes, I will agree to that."

After that he stood to his feet and shook my hand, asking me to, "Tell your mom I said goodbye."

"I will."

"I'll swing by here on Thursday, after school."

"See you then," I said.

And then he walked out.

That's all I can remember from that conversation, but I answered all his questions promptly without thinking of answers, and best of all truthfully.

I really can't imagine what my mom was feeling when she walked back into the kitchen. She wasn't angry, I'm sure she felt extreme fear that I had gotten myself into something very bad. I thought she'd be angry, but she sat at the table with me, and asked calmly while lighting her lady cigarette, "Well, what's that about, son?"

"Mom, I guess in the course of buying, I bought something that was stolen."

"I see, and when is Comb coming back?"

"Who is that, Mom?" I asked.

"Oh, that was his pet name. We all called him Comb, because of his fantastic head of hair, and I had trouble saying his first name."

"He said Thursday after school."

"You know we went to school together and he had a thing for me?"

"He did?"

"Yep," she said laughing nervously.

I was still shaking, but I tried to remain cool and thought to myself that these sorts of things must happen all the time. I sure was wrong about that.

I drove to the parsonage straight away and found Kenny leaning over a soldering iron.

"I need that Crown amp back right now, man !" I said.

"Really? I haven't fixed it yet."

"It's stolen and I need it for the cops."

"The cops?" Kenny asked.

"Yep, the cops were just at my house!"

"HOLY SHIT!"

"Come on, man," I said, "help me get it into the car."

He on one side and me on the other hoisted it into the trunk of my mom's car.

"Dave, you getting in trouble for this?" he asked.

"I don't know, man; I just don't know."

I got in the car and left.

What no one knew, not even my mother, was that Detective Underwood had been to the parsonage and had spoken with Kenny before he came to my house.

Kenny didn't meet the same detective I met. The man he met was angry, suspicious and extremely curt.

When Kenny let him in the front door of the parsonage, Detective Underwood had to step over mountains of clutter and the smell of cat urine pierced his nose. His eyes had darted from left to right and his head swiveled from first left, then right. From the moment he entered the parsonage he was a normal cop back on the midnight shift investigating something he knew with his nose wasn't right.

He was in firm possession of the ethos that street cops had, mixed with the nose of a detective which resulted in him never believing anything he heard and only half of what he saw.

Kenny, without any hesitation or pressure told the Detective that I had purchased the Amplifier and how much I had paid but he didn't know who I had purchased it from. When Detective Underwood asked him if I knew beforehand that it was stolen, he replied "yes."

Kenny then asked him, "Will Dave be arrested for this?"

Detective Underwood said, "Yes, David will be arrested and charged with receiving stolen property."

Kenny didn't incriminate himself by telling the detective that the Amp was just upstairs in his bedroom, instead he said he didn't know where the amp was at the time, but Dave knew where it was.

This act possibly made Kenny feel good about himself. This added to his self-hatred, in the form of schadenfreude. A boy with a father that didn't care about him, a missing mother, he felt all alone in the world when he needed to feel part of a family. Genie Productions had provided this fix temporarily, but since we had to have a crew to move the equipment it caused a rift between us. He was jealous of Lucinda and of Ed Longbow, and at the same time felt that the other members of the crew were beneath his station in life. He was allowed and supported by his father to drop out of the one thing that had given him structure and some amount of discipline in his life. School. Once school was out for him, Kenny spiraled emotionally out of control, while he desperately sought a means to feel better about himself.

I had parents that loved and cared for me, I had control of the business and the spotlight seemed to always fall on me despite him being taller and smarter. He felt this arrest would shift the spotlight, and bring me down to the ground.

It would have, had Detective Underwood not had a secret love for my mother.

Back at his headquarters and after a few phone calls, Underwood realized I was a full-time student, and Kenny was a delinquent dropout. It was also known by the Detective of Uncle Ivan's sexual proclivities, but not only that, he recognized how fast Kenny had asked about my arrest, which suggested to him something deeper must be afoot.

Since Kenny had dropped out of school he had started to hang around the skating rink in the mornings when he should have been in class. All of this information spoke volumes to Detective Underwood.

In the weeks and months preceding the stolen amp incident, my mother ever faithful and diligent in keeping our clothes clean, had found small wax paper bags in Kenny's pockets. These were the type of bags in which cocaine was sold.

OLD SPICE

Time slowed way down while I waited for Thursday. I went to school and did what I'd normally do. Ed Longbow and Lucinda knew something was wrong with me, but I kept my mouth shut on what had happened.

When I came from school that Thursday, I pulled into our driveway. I was surprised to see a shiny bronze late model unmarked police car pull up right behind me, like it had been following me.

I got out and walked over to the driver's side window, where Detective Underwood greeted me smiling and asked me to get in on the passenger side, not the backseat. The rule was that normally, the backseat of any police car was strictly reserved for those under arrest. The inside door handles in the back seats of police cars are disabled, and once you get in, there is no way out, unless someone opens it from the outside.

When I slid into the front seat I instantly smelled the calming and refreshing oaky fragrance of Old Spice after shave lotion mixed with Brylcreem hair tonic. The interior of his car was fastidiously clean and well organized. He thoughtfully turned the air conditioner up slightly as I looked around. There was a metal center console with a huge Motorola two-way police radio attached to it.

I saw black pens and sharp blue pencils that were neatly arranged in a cup holder, and a small plastic tray with a box of .38 bullets that sat on the passenger side seat.

"Just push those things to the side, Davey," he said smiling.

Detective Underwood's clothes also reflected how detail oriented he was. His white cotton collared shirt was starched to perfection. His grey suit pants were clean and perfectly creased, and his JC Penney suit jacket hung in the back seat from a wooden hanger.

The only wrinkles in his attire was from his blue steel snub nose .357 Magnum which was small but bulky sitting in a leather holster on his right hip.

"How has your day been, young man?" he asked.

"It's been good, sir, thank you!"

It was strange but in Detective Underwood's mind, he looked at me as the son he'd never had. He had imagined that if he had married my mother that she would have given him the son he'd always wanted. My mother was in possession of all the attributes he wanted in a woman. She was kind and covered in the smoothest skin he had ever seen, gorgeous legs, beautiful thick hair, and a bright smile he'd so desired in a woman; not only that, she was smart as a whip. Luckily, he also saw those attributes in me, I looked so much like my mother that he found himself wishing to call me son. Moreover, when he had walked into our home earlier in the week, it was clean, well decorated, brightly inviting and smelled of brewing coffee.

He and my mother had secretly dated for a year before she met my father, and before he began as a rookie with the police department.

But due to the racial climate at the time, he was told his career would have foundered if he had chosen to race mix. So instead he'd married a woman he found far less alluring. The woman he married was clumsy, messy and mean spirited, but she was white and he was told that was all that mattered. His wife had long since become grossly overweight at over 300 pounds, which according to her wasn't from overeating but due to a thyroid condition.

Also, she said that she was unable to have children which he found wasn't true, she just didn't want to have children.

But to see me for the first time and my temperament which he found impeccable was a delight to his eye. A tonic to his ear, when I spoke the truth to him when he questioned me earlier that week. He had so rarely heard truth spoken, it was refreshing to witness it. Of course, Kenny hadn't taken long to lie to him, which he expected.

When he had arrived at my house for his initial investigation he was surprised to find that the moment he witnessed my mother open the door, his hands got sweaty and his knees seemed to wobble. In that instant he without a shadow of a doubt knew that he still loved her. He was suddenly transformed back 26 years to their romance, and his intense feelings for her. He felt that her smile could still light up the room, and every nerve of his body quivered. He felt young again just hearing her voice!

He apologized for staring and said over and over again how she hadn't aged a day, and he meant every word.

My mother found that she still had feelings for him, mostly his sense of humor which had enthralled her. Twenty-six years earlier she had also kept her love for him a secret except for my uncle who though he knew of it didn't speak of it. She had prepared herself to tell my grandparents of this romance; she did expect some pushback from them, but she waited for his public proclamation which never came. Not long after he left her, she went on to college in North Carolina where she met my father who was larger than life itself and was quickly swept off her feet by his charisma.

When I walked into the house that first day my mother had been laughing so much she had forgotten the reason he was there. She trusted this man and also felt feelings of love reemerge for him. This he sensed and it made him feel like he was nineteen years old again.

But now he was back again. "Did you have time to get the amplifier, or should I come back later, son?"

"Yes, sir, it's in the trunk of my mom's car, but it's heavy, could you help me get it out please?"

"If it's so heavy how did you get it in the trunk, Davey?"

Once he asked this, he felt badly since he knew the answer already, but it was a conditioned reflex of all his years as an investigative officer. But since he had asked, he waited for the answer.

"It was at my Cousin Kenny's house, and he hadn't made time to even take it apart yet or really test it, so he helped me hoist it into the car."

Again I spoke the truth to him, and he felt his soul refreshed in hearing a young person utter it.

"No, I don't need it, but I'll need you to take it back from where it was stolen, if you have time?"

"Yes, sir, I have time."

"Do you know where the skating rink is?"

"Yes, next to Club Zanzibar?"

"Yes, the owner Mr. Russo is waiting for you."

"He's waiting now?"

"Yes, he's there waiting now, at the skating rink."

Then he added, "Before you go I will need you to sign this paper," which he produced on a metal clipboard with several copies, one white, one blue and the other yellow. All of the pages were typed and official with the State seal on them.

I glanced over the paper and I saw I was indeed fingering Henry Martinez for having possession of and selling stolen property. I also knew I could be charged for receiving stolen merchandise but for some reason I wasn't being charged. I quickly scribbled my name above where my name was typed and handed it back to him.

Not only was the Detective not charging me, he was still thinking fondly of my mom. I was sure that he knew that I didn't know it to be stolen when I purchased it, and even if I had suspected it stolen it was clear it was in bad shape and didn't work. I was making his job a bit easier, and the great discovery of seeing his old flame again was a double plus gain.

"Ok, Davey, thank you, and make sure you take the amplifier to the skating rink, alright?"

"Yes, sir, I'm leaving now."

"You don't have to leave right now," he said.

We sat in his car a little longer while he told me many stories of my mom and her time in high school playing basketball and running track. He also mentioned my mother's pet name which he thought had been long since forgotten. He fondly and lovingly referred to her then as "Duckie."

He smiled a great deal, and asked me questions like my father would, mostly about my future plans. He gave me a few of his business cards, and told me with great sincerity to call him if I ever needed anything at all.

I walked back into the house, and watched Detective Underwood quickly drive away.

I had seen many TV cop shows, and knew that the stolen property was supposed to go into evidence or something and not directly returned to the rightful owner. I thought his direction to return it a bit odd, but I wanted to just be done with all this craziness.

PRO HAC VICE

I did what he told me to do and drove straight over to Club Zanzibar in New Hampton Beach, which was right next to the skating rink.

New Beach Skating rink was a massive building with a smooth varnished wooden floor, that was completely open in the center and carpeted on the sides. Upon the carpeted sides were coin operated video games and arcade machines that lined every single wall, except where the skate rental booth and grille were. On a busy night it wouldn't be unusual to find 500 skaters rolling around to dance music on the smooth wooden floor.

Club Zanzibar had a Middle Eastern motif, like you might expect at a Sultan's palace. Pastel colors, silk curtains that separated faux silk couches. The 60 foot dance floor was outlined by sweeping and scrolling waist high walls. The walls were painted in Middle Eastern themes with camels and Arab women with veils.

Connecting the two establishments were two wooden porticos, that had a valet stand to assist with parking.

I had been to both places once or twice with my parents, but it wasn't a popular place for kids to hang out, it had since become known for a bad element to frequent, and had become slightly rundown and outdated.

The moment I drove up two large men, well over six feet tall, came out from the portico. One was wearing a blue two-piece suit and the other was wearing gym clothes which at the time were blue sweat pants, blue suede Pumas with a white stripe and a cotton Riverside High School polo shirt.

I was shocked and suddenly afraid when I recognized it was my gym teacher, Coach Don Marietti. I wanted to drive off and speed away, but instead I got out of the car and said, "I'm here to see Mr. Russo."

Coach Marietti was surprised to hear me say that name, and was confused for a moment, but he then nodded his head and said, "I know why you are here, Red."

"The amp is in the trunk," I replied nervously.

Once I opened the trunk, the big man in the blue suit looked in and then told the coach, "You carry that fucking thing in, *Fottuto Stronzo!*"

"You follow me, kid," said the big man in the blue suit.

The coach grabbed the amp using his great strength, and his immense meaty hands. I immediately closed the trunk and closely followed the big man in the blue suit through darkly tinted double glass doors and up a flight of stairs. The coach was behind us and I could hear him breathing hard and moaning with each step because of the weight of the ship's anchor amplifier.

We went into a central reception area that said "PRIVATE" in bold capital letters. From there I continued to obediently follow the big man in the blue suit.

After a brief knock we entered a small alcove and walked into a bright office, where my eyes and nose were quickly accosted by pungent cigar smoke. This office was completely out of place for that of a skating rink, it reminded me of the Kennedy Center or how the President of IBM's office might look. It was very odd to be in this sort of office in what seemed a cheap joint.

A small and very thin elderly man dressed in a light blue V-neck terrycloth shirt and dark grey seersucker pants, stood up and directed a smile toward me. The next thing I noticed was he wore a highly polished two inch solid gold Italian horn with a clasped twenty-two inch gold Figaro chain that hung down in amidst his long and wispy gray chest hair.

"Here's that red nigger, Mr. Russo," said Coach Marietti *derisively.* Mr. Russo instantly looked at him harshly, and Coach sheepishly left the room after putting the ship anchor amp down on the corner of the desk.

Two other men that were in the back of the room got to their feet once Mr. Russo extended his hand and smiled indicating for me to sit. His gestures were warm and inviting, but he had a coldness about him.

I sat in a large wingback leather chair in front of a huge ornate oak desk, like a bank manager would have. His desk was clean and nothing lay upon it except a mammoth square crystal ashtray. Perched on the side of the ornate ashtray lay a smoldering ten-inch hand rolled contraband cigar.

Mr. Alberticio Russo was bald with only a band of thick, greyish white hair around the fringe of his scalp. His face was smooth and ruddy without any wrinkles or blemishes. His long jaw was wide and prominently outlined his hairless chin. He was an older man of eighty-three years, but for an old man, his eyes blazed with the fiery red confidence of ten lifetimes. His teeth were sawed down like bright weeds toward the left, and his thin cardboard lips curled down to the right, and only straightened when his Cuban cigar was nestled within them.

"So nice to meet you, Davey, I've heard nothing but good things about you!" he said with a voice that sounded like his throat was full of ancient pebbles that resonated at command.

"You have? Thank you."

"Is this the gadget that Henry stole from us?" he asked in a well-educated version of English.

Heads nodded in the room.

"Davey, I'd like to thank you for delivering this to us today! We know you are busy with school and your music business.

Tell me," he said leaning back in the chair, "did you pay Henry Martinez $200 for it?"

When he asked me this, he like Detective Underwood already knew the answer. He knew the answers to all the questions he asked. He knew them in such studied detail that it was all merely a game for him to ask them.

"Yes," I easily confessed.

He reached into his back pocket, peeled ten $20 bills from a large wad of cash and slid them gently across the desk before putting the rest of the cash back in his pocket all in one smooth flawless motion. His nimble fingers counted the bills faster than any seasoned bank teller.

"Mr. Russo, I don't need the money back. I just wanted to make sure you got your property back."

"Did you hear that? This kid is not only smart but he's got morals!" he said laughing. His gravelly laugh filled the room, while the other men also laughed.

"Davey, this amp doesn't really belong to us, it belongs to the Club Leman."

Shocked and not really understanding what he meant, I kept quiet.

My father had long taught me to be quiet if I didn't completely understand what an adult meant.

"See, I told you, Sandy, this kid is smart, and did you see how he kept quiet? That's a sign of mental agility."

Sandy remained silent but shook his head slowly in acknowledgement.

Sandy Salucci sat alertly quiet in a wingback chair on the far side of the room and just behind Mr. Russo's desk. Santo "Sandy" Salucci was no longer a mere boy of thirteen years old. He now had a head full of hoary blondish hair, under which his eyes wore thick framed designer gazelle eyeglasses.

Sandy Santo Salucci was a handsome man, and remarkably fit to be now in his 50s. He didn't speak to me directly but his eyes never left their lock on my own. Santo had become the sort of man that dressed well every day, shaved every day and never went to the barber shop, but the barber came to his home in New Hampton Beach once a week to trim his hair. His dark grey silk suit fit very well across his shoulders, but due to recent events that had worried him, he had lost weight that cost him almost an inch in his waistline. This day he had a brand new belt to hold up his pants, but no one had seemed to notice. His white cotton shirt also was a bit loose in the neck which made his Windsor knot in his dark blue tie slump forward, which was noticeable to his group.

Long ago, Santo Sandy Salucci's greatest dream was fulfilled and with the help of Mr. Abraham Legatto he came to America and became a lawyer.

"Sandy" as he was called was now a lawyer by education but he was unable to pass the New York State bar exam, but had passed and been admitted to the Pennsylvania and the Florida Bar. Early on he worked as head of investigations for Abraham Legatto, Esq. while he took and failed five New York bar exams. These failures he blamed on the new format of the New York State Bar Exam. But if needed to he would appear in court to represent a client Pro hac vice, which was sanctioned with just a phone call to one of his judge friends.

Sandy Salucci wasn't a lawyer like Abraham Legatto. Sandy was not in possession of the gift that Legatto had with his voice and all of its attributes, like tone, ad lib remarks, and intonation. He wasn't a litigator. Sandy very seldom appeared in court and if he did, he was there as the second and not the lead.

Sandy's law practice was that of business dealing, which included national and international contract law and real estate. That's where the money was and where his unique talent lay. The other thing that made him uniquely different than Mr. Legatto, was his blood lust when weighing risk vs reward. Nothing was business for him, everything was personal which made him diabolically ruthless. Out of all the men in the room that day, Santo Salucci was the most dangerous.

Sandy was extremely effective for all of Mr. Legatto's legal clients due to his powers of persuasion. Which at times grew from the point of a pen, or the business end of a pistol during the middle of the night.

Salucci hated New York, and its climate. He moved to Florida after World War II and had begun a life with Mr. Russo's younger brother Ruben and his wife Mary. His job then was to oversee the day to day operations of three hotels in Coconut Grove, and Miami Beach.

The Russo family had a generational pedigree that had traced all the way back to Sicily. Prior to World War I, it was Ruben and Albertcio's grandfather that worked for Don Cologne in caring for his estate. Their grandfather Alphonse Russo worked with Don Biagateao's grandfather in Bisacquino, Sicily. They had grown rich together with just one caper of robbing robbers, it was just after this when Alphonse came to America and began or continued what would be his lifelong business of working in the dark shadows and fringes of the law.

In 1970, after the untimely death of Rueben Russo he took a job with the older Alberticio Russo near Allentown, Pennsylvania working directly with Bethlehem Shipping and Steel. He had been a contract lawyer with the Union for only three years when President Nixon allowed the import of cheaper steel into the U.S., which essentially killed the market and his fledgling legal career.

With their shipping and supply lines to South America intact, as well as to Libya and Europe from the floundering steel business, they moved their entire operation to New Hampton Beach where Ruben Russo had established a territory of bars, motels, and two restaurants. There they hit the ground running with loan sharking and illegal gambling, but got into the disco and dance club business to move and distribute all their tax-free booze, tax-free cigars and cigarettes. While loan sharking and gambling were their life blood, the disco business was blossoming into a true earner. It became a big earner due to the amount of cocaine they could move through their bars and dance clubs. One other highly secret business they were involved in, was the funeral business. Albert's Funeral Home helped them get rid of certain leftovers from bad business deals, or botched legal contracts. This was accomplished one piece at a time, or incinerated whole at 1800 degrees Fahrenheit.

They had direct shipping from South America to get all the highly refined cocaine they could sell. If they brought in fifty kilograms it would essentially be sold the moment it hit the street. Heroin was a bit more tricky since if not used the narcotic will decay and lose its efficacy within sixty days of its manufacture. It was Sandy who came up with the idea to give away the highly addictive drug for free, once its potency declined. He figured this was good for business, and it was, however the cocaine didn't have a shelf life, and the money they earned from it was cleaner.

Sandy's job was essentially to lube up the wheels of change by whatever means necessary. It could be pay offs, bribes, or even extortion but one way or another their agenda would be heard or felt. Sandy's handpicked people were in the police evidence room, all the way to the Mayor's Office not to mention sanitation, legal offices, and a Judge or two.

Not many people knew of Mr. Alberticio Russo, they knew only Sandy as the man in charge. However, this day Russo had decided to meet me in person, mostly due to how his inside man Detective Underwood had described me. Coach Don Marietti had also provided some insight.

There was utter quiet in the room, while Mr. Russo sat staring at the amp and puffing his large cigar.

It was at that very moment when a large, brown, fleet footed German roach climbed from within the amplifier's cooling vent and balanced itself on a cooling fan. Its long, threadlike and dark antennae twitched surveying its new surroundings, and then it began nimbly running down the power cord toward the clean oak desk.

"Sandy! Get Don in here to take this contraption off my desk!"

In a flash Coach Don Marietti walked in again and lifted the amp off his desk while two more of the striped brown leathery stowaways from the parsonage fell out of the amplifier.

One ran like greased lightning under Russo's desk, and the other took flight and flew across the room and landed on a far wall.

"Kill that fucking Scarafaggio!" yelled Sandy.

"What?"

"Omicidio that fucking Cock Roach!"

"Where?"

"The Fottuto Scarafaggio!"

By then the stealthy brown bug had disappeared beneath the ornate oak desk, under a lamp and to parts unknown.

Once Coach walked out, and the door was closed Mr. Russo began speaking.

"Kid, we don't want that apparatus, we want Henry Martinez, and got the cops involved to find him, and that's how we found you."

When he said the name Henry Martinez, there was an inflexion in his voice, but not any old change of tone. When he uttered that name, I could hear and feel sheer angst.

Again I stayed silent which Mr. Russo for some reason really liked.

"Davey, this is a war! When those people opened the cabaret and casino, they cut our business here over 78% per quarter!"

Mr. Russo was speaking about the Pasqotouk Indian Nation. They secretively owned and operated Club Leman. In the years past when Ruben Russo ran this territory the tribal council was docile, compliant and easy to manipulate. However, in the years since his brother had taken over, many changes had occurred within the Pasqotouk Nation.

Their police force of 122 full-time uniformed officers, and a secret squad of "Mitaaswi Animosh."

The "Mitaaswi Animosh" or loosely translated "Ten Dogs" were problem solvers and not sworn officers but a group of armed militia, or regulating party. They were a judge and jury all built into one and an extremely effective arm of tribal law.

Anything or anyone that was, "endangering the peace and lives of the citizens of the nation" was eradicated with extreme prejudice. Not only that, they had a secret expense budget, and the full support of all the tribal officers if needed.

These ten highly trained Native men operated outside all rules, regulations and guidelines set forth by the tribal council. They had all been handpicked by Mr. E. J. Longbow and only he knew their identities.

From narcotics, illegal loans, or outside agitators the individual suspected of any of this and with sufficient evidence, within the nation or outside the nation would simply vanish. The "Mitaaswi Animosh" also had secret handpicked confidantes within the police, the courts, lending institutions and local government.

They took care of the nastier bits of society that come along with owning and operating hotels and casinos.

It was speculated that these men didn't live on the reservation but were flown or floated in when needed from the State of North Dakota.

Not only that, they had a direct connection to the federal courts with four federal lawyers they retained full-time. So the normal kick in the door tactics of Russo's organization didn't faze them. If you pushed them, they pushed back, it was that simple now!

The actions of this secret group was what had caused Santo Salucci to lose almost 15 pounds in less than six months. Santo knew something was different for a few years, but it was becoming more and more apparent and try as he may it simply made no sense to him. The contacts he had within City Hall and the police department had simply vanished, those who didn't vanish had become blithering idiots and sent to state run nursing centers.

"Mitaaswi Animosh" in times past had shoot-outs with local or state police, local gangs, and even the sheriff's department, after which they just vanished into thin air; witnesses reported they just "flew away."

Santo suspected it was perhaps the Irish or another Sicilian organization that had wandered into the Russo's business area, but none of the normal signs were there. Santo felt as though he was waging war with ghosts that appeared out of the mist and then disappeared.

When Mr. Russo said the word "WAR" I could see his face turning red, and anger oozed into his words.

"We had it solved by paying Henry Martinez to shut it down from the inside, instead he took our money, almost 50 grand the Granchi Traditori and then robbed them and disappeared the *Fottuto Stronzo!*" When he said this he slammed his hand on the desk violently and stood up. Once he stood the other men in the room stood up, all except Sandy who finally spoke to Mr. Russo softly and said , "Mal commune, mezzo Gaudio."

Russo nodded his head and sat back down acknowledging what Sandy had just said.

The man with all the answers had no tolerance for anything that didn't go as he had planned.

For that instant Mr. Russo had made another error, his emotions led him to revealing a truth that existed in his game plan. He had not planned to say what he had said to me, which was revealing the plan to shut down the Club, and how he'd gone about doing it. His emotions had got the best of him in that few seconds, when his thoughts overflowed and material-ized into speech.

The room grew utterly quiet again and the fire in his eyes had flared and now was settling while he stared at me calmly and politely.

I sat nervously trying to glean what I could of what was go-ing on. I didn't understand it and my head felt light. The room spun slowly as I searched the eyes of those around me. They seemed to be dark, lifeless doll eyes. Huge men without souls, dangerous men that seemed to have sworn allegiance to the devil himself, and by doing so left this world. I wasn't smart at that age, I was innocent and had only lived a life beyond my teen years through my parents' teachings. Genie Productions had provided fun, money and excitement, but here I sat within the fringe of a deadly breech. These were surely monsters that I sat with. Not the ones in the storybooks, but the ones that actually walked the earth among us.

The meeting was over and I was allowed to leave. I wish I could say I left as I arrived, but something had happened to me in that room. I somehow had aged ten years in less than thirty minutes, and my eyes were beginning to open.

I thought as I drove, how did Russo know it was $200 for the amp? Why did Detective Underwood insist that I take the amp to Mr. Russo, and not to the police evidence locker?

Unknown to just about everyone at that time, Detective Underwood worked part-time for Sandy Salucci. Sandy didn't like the police at all and still referred to them as "The Murderous Carabinieri." When dealing with them, he always thought of them as completely disposable, and his distrust of them intensified with how loyal they claimed to be. Santo Sandy Salucci was still haunted by the ghosts of the past, and how his parents had been murdered by the police and were solely responsible for the disappearance of his brother Marcello not to mention what they did to Anna Dotatto and her family. However, now he would use them until he got what he needed from them. only then he would certainly "Nutrire i maiali con i maiali," "feed pigs to pigs."

The unvarnished truth that Santo Sandy Salucci never told anyone was that he didn't like or trust Detective Underwood at all, nor did he like or trust Coach Don Marietti, partly due to how loquacious they were.

After the Martinez problem, Coach had told them a long and protracted story of two niggers in his locker room who he had to "Fuck up" and had mentioned my name. Detective Underwood, who attended the same meeting mentioned that he knew my mother, and went on a tirade about his love affair with her. Sandy listened politely to all of this, but in his heart he knew that these two "Granchi Codardi" would be placed in a pot very soon, once Mr. Russo closed his eyes. However, in the meantime he would work with them, cautiously.

In the days and weeks after the stolen amplifier incident, Kenny changed a great deal. I'd like to say it was a slow change in his behavior and perhaps I had gotten so busy that I was unaware. Whatever it was, Kenny changed drastically !

We wouldn't see Kenny at all on Tuesday evenings for our get together. We began seeing him only at the club during the weekends. He wouldn't come in with us to set up the music, but only came in with a smile, would greet everyone, and then leave to roam around the club.

It wasn't just his new behavior but Kenny's clothes were different. Kenny had abandoned his white on white Adidas tennis shoes, and sweat suits like we had all worn, and now dressed in silk suits with alligator shoes when he appeared at the club. He wore a massive diamond pinky ring on his left hand and had an assortment of Members Only jackets that he wore with slacks and some sort of lizard but very expensive cowboy boots. His walk and talk changed, and while he waved the diamond ring around you could see his manicure. His haircut was different and it wasn't just cut now, but styled with some sort of hair gel.

He had a new set of friends that followed him around like ducklings.

Kenny did come to a Tuesday night get together in our basement with three older women and some strange looking guy friend of his. Kenny wore a beautiful olive colored silk suit and a white Brooks Brothers brushed cotton shirt with an open collar. Kenny's neck was adorned with several large gaudy gold chains. One chain was a thick serpentine, the other was a Cuban link frosted with crushed diamonds.

He didn't look at the equipment or ask how it was working. He no longer brooded while nursing a beer, he was animated and bragging about how much money he had, or where he was going shopping in the days to come.

Coon Skin was really taken by his wardrobe and took interest and asked him questions while complimenting his "finery." Soon we all went outside at Kenny's behest to see a stretch Cadillac limousine and chauffeur he had hired for the night.

Kenny snapped his fingers and the chauffeur got out and opened the doors for us. We all climbed inside and looked around at the limo's fine and luxurious appointments. Kenny sat with his head up and loved this new station he had achieved in life. We all sat in the car while Kenny began to explain how much his wardrobe cost while he flashed cash for us all to see. The crew and Kenny's new friends went on a quick ride around the block in the limo. We had only driven ten minutes before Kenny said he had an emergency and he kicked us out of the limo in front of Mule Train's house. He rudely rushed us all out of the limo and we stood on the curb and watched the big luxurious vehicle speed away.

I loved the car, but deep in my heart wondered what all this was about, and he seemed so completely different.

When he came to the club around midnight he and his cronies arrogantly strode to the front of the line and were allowed to walk right in as a member of Genie Productions, but he estranged himself from us all more and more.

Weeks earlier Kenny had a meeting with Coach Marietti at the behest of Sandy Salucci. The meeting was informal and just a couple of hockey players shooting the shit over a few beers in the private area of the skating rink. Coach Don gave Kenny two stacks of fifty small wax bags bound together by a rubber band, of slightly cut cocaine. He explained it was a free sample and he wanted feedback of its quality. He explained that he could do whatever he wanted with the powder, and contact him day or night if he needed more. Once Kenny put them in his pocket, Coach changed the subject and once again began to speak of hockey.

It was the research that Santo Sandy Salucci had done for Mr. Legatto long ago, that opened and exposed the truth of Kenny's mother Helen. How she had fled the scene and where she had wound up. A member of a neo Nazi organization in Idaho. Sandy also knew of Kenny's father and his sexual proclivities with underage males. Knowing all of this Sandy knew just what Kenny needed if he should ever need to use him as a pawn in this sinister chess game of his.

From the first dose of cocaine he took, which came directly from Coach Don Marietti, Kenny felt warm inside and all of his problems instantly vanished.

Kenny's new job? It was to supply cocaine to the club-goers at Lemans on the weekends. During the week he moved cocaine and set up small dealers around the area to sell for him. Sales of cocaine were then at an all-time high! He secretly was using a large portion of his earnings to feed his own habit.

Cocaine made Kenny feel warm inside, it replaced the feelings of despair from what was going on with his mother and father. It became his new family.

Cocaine entered Kenny's nose and was absorbed by the mucous membranes of his sinuses, there it entered his bloodstream, and affected his brain chemistry. It wasn't a head high Kenny felt, it was something called a body high which warmed and soothed him. He felt so good in fact that he had instantly forgotten what it was that made him feel this way. This reverse amnesia is one of those little understood properties of cocaine, which separates it from the clumsiness of booze or the hypnotizing effects of marijuana. The end user of cocaine forgets that it is cocaine that has caused the good feelings, and the brain blocks the action and cause, until which time the user needs more. At that time the user simply thinks he wants more of the powder and not that it is needed to continue the high. Like most drugs with this effect, the feeling of the first high is something that will be chased throughout the time of its use, and the subtle transformation from use to abuse.

It is this body high that helps the user lose inhibitions that are built in to protect from certain perceived threats. It gives confidence, and increases awareness to the point of it being distorted. This is why it's very popular at clubs where there is dancing, or even sports. The user becomes nimble, hyper aware, and overconfident in their abilities, in a way no other substance offers.

Without Kenny, I brought up Coon Skin and Mule Train to run the lights for us, while Meals on Wheels and I mixed in the music. The club seemed much more intense in those days. The crowds were larger, with twice the energy they once had.

Security was doubled and the cover charge shot up to $75.

DEATH & TAXES

By 1980, I finally had hair under my arms, a frog's hair mustache and stood six feet tall. I wore my hair very short, and my muscles had begun to grow.

Lucinda and I were finally having sex together and we became almost inseparable in school, however this didn't stop me from seeing some of the grown women that came to the club, or at least calling them. My mother had a separate phone line put in my room, which at the time was a BIG DEAL!

It was difficult to resist the overtures of young women in their 20s with perfect hourglass figures, and driving beautiful sports cars. I enjoyed my time with them an evening a week, but wouldn't let myself get too deeply ensconced with that lifestyle. I had adhered to my father's teachings on staying focused on what I wanted to do in the future. My mother was well pleased to see me with women other than Lucinda. She said it was healthy to not become overly entwined with her or anyone at 17 years old.

One night I was out with an older woman that I had met at Club Leman. We met at Alberton's Italian Restaurant in New Hampton to have dinner and get to know each other a bit better. I was shocked and surprised to see sixteen year old Mule

Train there having dinner with two older women from the club. The instant he saw me he smiled like a Cheshire cat, I gave him a quick smile and a wink and we both continued to enjoy our respective female company. We never spoke of this encounter, but I did notice a slight change in Mule Train. He seemed more relaxed, and began wearing nicer clothes.

After not seeing or even hearing from Kenny in many weeks I stopped by the parsonage, to see if he was there. The Reverend I.C Guise came to the door and smiled at me. When I asked if Kenny was home, he began animatedly bragging that Kenny had moved out and was now living in New Hampton Beach in a waterfront condo. He went on about how fancy it was and in the midst of this he gave me the exact address.

From the parsonage I drove directly to the address the Reverend gave me, I saw the Oldsmobile sitting in a parking spot and I knew I was at the right place.

A quick knock on the door and a scantily clad, statuesque, and beautiful older woman who appeared to be at least 30 years old opened the door. I asked for Kenny. She asked my name and who I was and I told her I was his first cousin Dave. Apparently she had not heard about me, but she kindly let me in before she asked me to please take off my shoes which I quickly did and then I obediently followed her to the living room .

The house smelled brand new, new carpet smell and fresh paint smell soothed my nose. As I was following her I could see from the light in front of her how sheer her gown was, and could see her entire womanly nude body very easily. In the living room on a white leather sectile couch, where he sat in the middle with his feet propped up on a solid glass coffee table with bronze colored corners, I saw Kenny wearing what I can only describe as a dark green and red silk kimono that was open and uncinched. A super large TV was on with some sporting event but the sound was down and Kenny was on the phone yelling at someone on the other end.

There was an entertainment center with the TV as the centerpiece and many new high end Japanese electronics with names I had never heard of, large reel to reel and cassette decks and equalizers. A turntable similar to the ones we used was sitting on a glass shelf surrounded by albums that said "promotional copy." When Kenny saw me his face lit up and he came over and gave me a hug before he realized his kimono was uncinched and quickly cinched the silk belt. We stood looking at each other for a few moments before he said, "Let me give you the tour." At the same time, he snapped his fingers and said, "Yvette, bring us drinks out on the patio." She smiled and nodded her head without uttering a word.

I followed Kenny upstairs while he spoke very rapidly of the artwork that hung in the stairwell, and when we got to the second floor he pointed to his bedroom, and described his new bed which was a California king, and how much it cost. We walked into the room, and four huge sliding glass doors with views of the ocean just out back. We stood there a few moments, admiring the view, and then he took me to the other room which he called his office. He had a small desk, with a nice desk lamp, pens and papers, and just below the desk was a massive black safe with a combination dial on it. He pointed that out and said it was full of cash, and he was shopping for another one. The room had a desk chair, and a leather pull-out futon, and a smaller double sliding door that faced the ocean. Just off that room was a full bathroom.

"Bet you have never seen anything like this before have you, Dave?"

The house was beautiful and featured thick bright white wall to wall Berber carpets. Back downstairs he pointed out some of the appliances he had in the kitchen, while Yvette was preparing drinks, and this time I could see her ample breasts swaying as she stood shaking up cocktails. Kenny and I went on the balcony and there we sat on two large wicker chairs with soft white cushions with a blue and green ceramic tiled and wrought iron table between us. Each mosaic tile featured seashells, gulls, fish and crabs.

We sat quietly while we both stared at the ocean and listened to the waves which were furious that day.

I got right to the point, and told Kenny that we all missed him and wished he could come back and help or at least visit us.

He stayed silent, like he hadn't heard me. I told him I missed him and loved him and then asked him if he would please stop in once in a while to see us. Again, total and uncomfortable silence, and then the drinks arrived.

Yvette had a small sterling silver tray with two large Bloody Mary's in tall glasses with celery stalks protruding out, that she sat on the table and then took one glass off and handed it to Kenny and then the other to me. The wind blew her sheer gown close to her body and it was impossible not to see her womanly beauty at that point. As I noticed this, Kenny saw me notice her and he smiled.

He rudely snapped his fingers and told her she was dismissed. She smiled and elegantly walked back inside while we both watched her, admiring her great beauty. Once she slid the glass door shut we began sipping the drinks.

There was this very odd and uneasy feeling between us, like we were strangers and I was meeting him for the very first time; however, at least with a stranger there would be polite conversation.

The ocean roared very loudly behind us and I began to mention the time we had been in Montauk and the waves were similar and he had saved my life. Remember?

"I don't know if I ever thanked you for that, man," I told him, "so I'm thanking you right now!"

He responded by telling me about Yvette and her age and how they had met. He said he met her at the club one night and how she worshiped him. When I heard this I smiled and said, "Why are you surprised?" Kenny thought about this response for a few, but now moved to ask me how I had found him.

I explained I went to the parsonage and had spoken to his dad. Again he remained silent.

"Yeah, Dave, you need a lot of money to live here," he said sure of himself.

"I can see that, man," I said nodding my head in agreement.

185

Kenny stayed silent and we continued sipping our drinks.

I told him again how much we all missed him and told him that even my mom missed him. This time I told him with my heart and not my head, and as I spoke my eyes began welling up, and my throat had a large lump forming.

It was at this moment Yvette came back out holding the phone, and sat it down in front of him.

He quickly thanked me for coming and told me that Yvette would see me out and he had to take the call. I felt awful, I didn't know if I should yell at him, curse him or just begin hitting him. My heart was broken seeing him and feeling him treat me this way, and at that age I didn't understand his curt behavior toward me. It cut my very soul, and hurt in places I didn't know could hurt.

Yvette walked me to the door and I left wiping the tears from my face and angry that I felt vodka began coursing through my veins.

That same year my father wasn't home very often at all. His new position at White Sands Military base in New Mexico kept him away, or so he said.

Around this time , Lucinda and I came home at dawn and the kitchen just wasn't right. Normally my mom, without fail would have our dinner sitting neatly under aluminum foil sitting on the stove. But this time there was no food, instead there were wineglasses in the sink, and my expensive wine bottles in the garbage can. The kitchen smelled of Brylcreem, and oaky Old Spice aftershave. In the living room, old albums from music of the 1950s were out of their jackets, the stereo was left on, and my mom was passed out in her bed asleep. Lucinda and I didn't speak of this, we simply went into my room, closed the door and went to sleep.

Not long after this, while in the Riverside High School parking surrounded by tribe members, a dark figure moved through the crowd. I was confronted by a grown man who had illegally come onto school property, and was carrying an aluminum baseball bat. His name was Alex Martinez, the 21 year old younger brother of Henry Martinez. He was there to beat my head in for fingering his brother for the stolen amplifier. He was one of Kenny's cocaine customers, who became a low level dealer.

I was paralyzed with fear while he yelled at me waving the bat in my face. I had never felt fear like that before. It was a different fear than from the detective. It was a primal fear of death, which made my heart race out of control and my underarms got bristly.

I remember very clearly Ed Longbow saying to him, "I sure hope that bat is made out of chocolate 'cause you are going to eat that motha fucka."

Ed disarmed him very easily, while the Riverside High School security police grabbed him and held him in custody for the real cops.

Alex Martinez was arrested for trespassing, and during the search of his person, nine wax paper bags of white powder were discovered in his pockets, as well as four envelopes that contained a brown pungent leafy substance. With this discovery the Riverside cops had probable cause to search his car. There they found a switchblade knife , three more bags of white powder, and a SAII Crown amplifier that had been listed stolen by Club Lemans earlier that year.

With all this evidence and facing jail time he began to sing like a bird. He told the investigating detective everything he knew. The powders came from Club Zanzibar, the plot to shut down Lemans, as his brother Henry had described to him, and of a man named Sandy upstairs at the skating rink, and of course all about my Cousin Kenny.

The interviewing detective was none other than the well dressed, clean shaven and oaky scented Colmazio "the Comb" Underwood.

The next day Kenny was instructed to contact Albert's Bail Bonds, and put up the $5,000 for Alex Martinez's release. Which he did very promptly, and Alex went right back home to continue sacking and selling cocaine.

187

This event more than anything else made me see that the business I was in was a very dangerous one. Also recognizing how crucial it was to be a part of a group of peers, and in my case the no nonsense members of the tribe and my lifelong friend Ed Longbow.

A week later, a jogger in our local park found a human head lying beside the road. It was the severed head of Alex Martinez. Just days after that the body of Henry Martinez was discovered by a fisherman floating in the Matipan River.

The media, initiated during this time a hypnotic phrase to belay the fears of the general public when reporting certain deaths. The violent death of any of a Black or Brown person was "Drug Related." Later it would evolve into "Gang Related."

This small but powerful post script worked its way through all of our society, as well as the Criminal Courts.

Coach Don Marietti was a person of interest in these gruesome murders, and as eyewitnesses came forward, he was promptly arrested and held in the county jail awaiting trial.

TWO LINES OPEN
AND NO WAITING

In 1944 Rueben and Mary Russo of Philadelphia welcomed young Santo into their small three-bedroom home. Santo had his own room for the first time, clean sheets and a real wooden floor beneath his feet and roof over his head. He walked from room to room looking up and down in amazement that this was his new home.

The Russo's were childless and Mary went out and bought all the things she thought a 13 year old boy would like in his room, baseballs and mitts, a football, train set, car model and best of all a new 4-speed English racer bicycle. All of these things Santo loved, and was thankful to have, but best of all there was peace and a chance for a normal life. But what was a normal life? He didn't know at the time nor would he ever.

Mary enrolled him in school later that year and Santo was completely lost since his English was so poor. The next thing they did was hire an English tutor that would come over the house daily and work with him on English, history and math.

Rueben, who had only been in the United States five years also had great trouble with the language, but had jobs working at the Pittsburg shipping port. In his spare time he worked for his older brother Alberticio who had been in America since the first war and controlled a few businesses in Miami Florida. His claim to fame and his major money making was running liquor from 1924 to 1930.

One of the most captivating things Rueben and young Santo shared were the teachings from Don Biagateao. Years earlier, Rueben Russo had been promoted through the ranks of the Riservasi and served Don Biagateao with any of the businesses he had then in Gangi, Sicily, and even now he was the head of the American Riservasi.

The organization was simple, he loaned money, he owned prostitution houses and gambling spots, and provided enforcement of anyone willing to pay his fee, and of course dabbled in heroin sales and importation.

While Santo went to school to learn and further his education, he went on runs and jobs with Rueben. He was happy that he was part of something he had always aspired to which was to be part of the Riservasi, though he wouldn't have to climb down any steep cliffs with the .30 caliber machine gun, he simply became of age. Belonging to this group somehow would settle the score he had with the murders of his mother and father.

By the time he was 19 years old Santo spoke English fluently, and was beginning his first year at the University of Pittsburg. Occasionally he faced a type of bigotry when his professors or classmates used slurs when addressing him or other Italians. He would remain silent, and would simply smirk as he was taught. If they continued with it, they simply "fell down steps or had car accidents."

He stayed in contact and wrote letters to Abraham Legatto who was back in New York in his Legal practice after the war. Santo Salucci was the intermediary between Abraham Legatto and Don Biagateao, who now was 67 years old and was the Minister of transportation of Sicily.

190

COFFEE IS KING

In May of 1980, along with the eruption of Mount St. Helens, the small town of Horse Neck reported 315 deaths from cocaine overdoses, which made national news. Our high school claimed 18 of those deaths. A month later what also made national news was when comedian Richard Pryor set himself on fire and almost died while free basing cocaine.

The city, county and state prosecutors set up a task force to wage war against this epidemic.

Detective Sergeant Underwood was promoted to Captain and headed up the multi-jurisdictional drug interdiction team.

The first place they set their sights upon? Club Lemans in Horse Neck. They set their sights on Lemans, due to a new law on search and seizure which loosely said that *any* money, cars, homes or property found with drugs could be seized without any questions, if they contained or were used for drug sales, or distribution.

Mainstream white society never actually cared about drugs and their usage at clubs or parties. They disregarded it as something that the minorities in their communities indulged in. If they were not minorities that indulged, then it was the poorer whites who also occupied their time with this self-destructive behavior. These sentiments were reflected in the police departments as well. But the police department could make a show of force against drugs and satisfy some of their departmental needs at the same time.

What did the police need?

What the entire police precinct needed more than guns, bullets, dogs, or patrol units, *was a coffee machine.* During roll call no matter the subject, who was missing, who got shot, or any other issue, the lack of sufficient coffee was always on the agenda for all three police shifts. It was this that caused them, more than anything else to assemble to wage war against drugs!

It was very obvious this was money that the task force could use for furthering their cause, with the recent changes in search and seizure laws. Along the way, if they had any other unmet departmental needs, it could be cured without any eyebrows being raised.

July 18th, 1980, was like any other Friday night for myself, Wheels, Coon Skin, Mule Train and The Bootleg Brothers. The only difference was that we had a private party near New York City to perform.

I knew this venue and had been there before, and since we were without Kenny I was forced to move others into his job.

We all arrived at the Club at 8 p.m., and began to get things set up for the night. One of the bartenders handed me a small folded piece of paper. It was a small register receipt from Feathers Beverage and Liquor, and all it said was: "Noosh Mamadji Onagoc." It was from Ed Longbow telling me he was with his dad for the night.

Since I wouldn't be there we left Coon Skin with the night's playlist, confident that he and Mule Train could pull it off without a hitch, and they had Wendy there to assist them. We reviewed what songs they would play in which order, and for how long. We also reviewed the light show and which lights would be best for certain songs. Mule Train had it all in his mind of what he wanted to play, and we had heard him mix in the basement and liked his choice of music even if it wasn't exactly my own.

We got the music playing and reviewed the fog machine controls, the volume and equalizer settings with Mule Train who was laughing and kept saying, "I know, I know." It was straight forward, every knob and switch had been labeled with the magic marker by Kenny. However, the markings were smeared and difficult to read, but Train had seen us do the show many times, and I had confidence he could pull it off.

The rest of us left in the Genie Love van for the city and played at the party until 3 a.m. What a beautiful place that was, and what an amazing time we all had. I remember this night very well, it was the first time the Bootleg Brothers helped play the music with Wheels while Lucinda and I sat by relaxing. Lucinda and I danced to some of Barry White's love music we had played privately. We had practiced dancing for many months at this point.

It was very nice to enjoy the music and not be on the business end of it. The crowd was slightly older and they were all on their best behavior that night. The drive was smooth and no traffic at all to speak of. We collected our money and headed home.

Lucinda and I walked into the house at dawn, and found my mother sitting at the kitchen table.

She was happy to see us, more than she ever had been before. She hugged us both and began explaining that Wendy had called her and gave her the news of the club being raided by the cops.

Kenny, Mule Train and Coon Skin were arrested and thrown in jail.

I was shocked and speechless! She said, with tears in her eyes that she had been calling my dad all night and there was no answer, and she had been calling her brother Ivan, and he also was nowhere to be found.

The first thing we did was shower and change clothes before driving to the jail with the bail money.

We discovered that Coon Skin's bail was $500 cash or bond. Mule Train's bond was also set by the magistrate at $500, and we quickly paid their bail with the cash my mom gave us.

At 7 a.m. Lucinda and I anxiously waited in the Genie Love van for them to be released. The first to be released was Mule Train. This was Mule Train's first run in with the law, and he handled it very well to be such a young kid. I think he was in mild shock, but as soon as he asked me to stop at the deli on the way home, I figured he would be ok.

Fifteen minutes later Coon Skin came out smiling and singing, stating he was having a good time in the county jail, with *"My peeps upun Dhere."*

We inquired about Kenny to bail him out and found that his bail was set at $1,000,000. Which was shocking!

On the way home, Mule Train and Coon Skin told us the events of the night and the timeline.

They said it was a big night, the club was full, the bar was busy, Mule Train was in the middle of mixing *Good Times by* Chic, when the cops broke in with shotguns, raided the joint and they arrested everyone in sight. Mule Train said they arrested him only after he didn't know how to turn the music off and the main lights on.

The police had a difficult time arresting Mule Train. It wasn't because he resisted the police, it was simply due to his size. The arresting officer was unable to get handcuffs to fit Train's wrists. It took three more officers to figure out how to restrain him. They used four sets of handcuffs, ratcheting the chrome ring around each of his wrists which could only make one click. They used two more sets of cuffs as extensions, and hooked them to his belt loops near his back, since his arms were so massive. Then the problem was getting him into the police bus, since he would not fit through the narrow front door. Three officers pushed him into the doorway, and he simply would not fit. One of the smarter officers said, "How the hell are we gonna get him off the bus if we get him in there?"

After a bit of arguing they decided to sit him in the back of a police pickup truck, which had transported the drug dog to the club. Mule Train rode all the way to county jail in the bed of a pickup truck, while "Bambino" the drug dog licked his face and his neck, then rolled in his lap, then went back to licking his face. Mule Train loved this and giggled the entire way to the jail.

Coon Skin said he was arrested for, "Ov-jest –Dik-Scription," for giving false information. It took me thirty seconds but I figured he meant Obstruction of Justice, most likely since they didn't understand a word he said.

Wendy who was also there, wasn't arrested but was briefly questioned. It was determined she was far too pretty to be arrested but she was given the names and telephone numbers of several officers in case she had any questions. She was then given a ride home in the front seat of a police car.

After the arrests, and in central booking it was discovered that Mule Train was only sixteen, and Coon Skin was nineteen years of age. With this discovery their charges were reduced to disorderly conduct.

Mule Train went on to say that Kenny had major weight on him, and was looking at major time. When he and the others left for the jail, they all witnessed Kenny's car being torn apart and bags of drugs being removed.

That night in total the cops seized five kilograms of cocaine, ten pounds of marijuana, fifteen Cadillacs, a dozen Range Rovers, nine late model Mercedes-Benzes, eight Porsches, two Ferraris, one royal blue 1973 Oldsmobile Convertible and $389,000 in cash.

The cops also emptied out Mr. Longbow's liquor closet while looking for drugs, after gaining entry with a chainsaw. Not one bottle made it to the police evidence locker. Instead it was all taken to a storage unit for further processing as per Captain Underwood's instructions.

They cured their budget woes with one bust. Not only did they get the coffee maker, they had the best money could buy. The local cops got new cars, new vests, new weapons, and placed an order for a tank. It wasn't a real tank, but an Army surplus armored personnel carrier.

Just a few hours after we bailed out Mule Train and Coon Skin, Lucinda, Ed Longbow and I took the six-hour long SAT exam in the high school gym.

On Monday morning my mom and I sat on a brown thickly bolstered leather couch in the waiting room of Mr. Leo Strassenberg, ESQ, who had just one year ago taken over the practice of Abraham Legatto who had suddenly died after sixty-years of legal practice. My parents loved Mr. Legatto, who had the sense and presence of mind to set up his office above The Bear Claw Bakery in town. This meant it always smelled good in the office, and well into the parking lot. This caused his clients to stay a little longer for their appointments, and since he charged by the hour, well you get the picture.

My parents were Leo's first clients, and like Legatto they trusted his opinion. What I didn't know was that my mom had called Leo on Saturday morning, and he had already begun on the case.

I had already met Mr. Strassenberg, he was one of those that attended Kenny's 16th birthday party some years ago.

Leo was a short man, standing barely 5 foot 4 inches tall even with his high dollar shoe lifts, but the thing that stood out about him was his toupee. It was a mess of faux blond hair. His hair appeared as though a wild raccoon and a dust mop had a sexual tryst, and forty-five days later out popped this retromingent clump of disheveled hair that now had taken up residence atop Leo Strassenburg's head.

Leo's desk was a cluttered mess of yellow legal pads, cigarette butts, stray staples, and paper clips. His waste paper can was overflowing, and the office was in general disarray. There were no secretaries typing, the long hallway of books was covered in dust, and many of the books were off the shelves and sat on the floor. The windows and walls were now tinged and yellow from cigarette smoke.

With no one there to take the calls, the phone rang continually and his answering machine would take the call and we could hear very plainly his outgoing message and the private messages that were being recorded.

Leo had the sniffles and wiped his nose from time to time with a blue handkerchief in his lap. Occasionally he'd wipe it with the back of his hand not realizing it while speaking his legal jargon to us.

Leo and my Mom exchanged pleasantries, before he got right to the point.

"With regard to Mack Tanner, AKA Mule Train, and James Edward Varnoski, AKA Coon Skin, I had all their charges dropped this morning," said Mr. Strassenberg with a high pitched clownish tone of speech.

"However, Kenny Guise and the state's charges against him are beyond my expertise, and he will need a criminal specialist."

Mr. Strassenberg went on to say how they don't come cheap, and how much it could possibly cost, and with the evidence they had against Kenny it looked positively grim.

Mr. Strassenberg had secretly wished Legatto alive again, due to his ability to make things happen or not happen. Strassenburg worshiped Legatto and never knew exactly how he got things done, but always suspected that he must have had an inside man in some of the offices around town. Once he took over the legal practice of Legatto he had scoured the notes and case books that remained, but they had all been cleaned up secretly by Santo Salucci beforehand. Nevertheless, Strassenberg took over one of the most exclusive legal practices in the state, and he planned to take it to the next level, at least that was his thinking.

With the aromatic smell of fresh bread being baked just below us, Strassenberg explained to us in great detail the state's charges.

Kenny was being charged with, possession to distribute, possession with intent to sell, and possession of drug paraphernalia which included a scale, plastic sandwich bags, spoons and pipes.

The state also added something called, "aggravating circumstances," to the list of egregious charges. These charges came into play when drugs were sold close to schools, or public places used for social gatherings.

The aggravating circumstances spelled out that less than one mile away was the burned down high school of the Paquotank Tribe. Also, a public swimming pool was two blocks away, closed for the season but that still counted as an aggravating circumstance. All this meant my cousin was looking at 15-20 years in prison.

When he said this, my mother began crying and I had to get her some water and a cool cloth for her head.

Mr. Strassenberg began to speak with me, to ease the conversation away from the bitter pill he'd just served and asked me about school, and how my grades were, and what plans did I have for the future. When I spoke to him, and he praised my schoolwork, my mother slowly came back to a state of calm collectivity.

I told him that I would have been there that night had we not been called away to another gig near the city.

He told me that Lemans would be closed for the foreseeable future and it was a good thing that I wasn't there that night, since they arrested just about everyone.

Later that day my parents had a heated discussion on the phone, about Mom's idea to remortgage the house to get Kenny out of jail.

This was the exact moment that my father pulled a card he had been saving for a long time for a moment just like this, as he was almost sure to need it. He mentioned the bagel shop, and the printing business, and the amount of money they had wasted on her family. So now he for the first time threatened her with divorce.

Before I knew it my mom was packing her things, to fly to New Mexico to try to smooth things over with him. This all happened in less than 36 hours, my mother left me with blank signed checks, cash, her credit card, and told me to behave and that Cousin Betsy and Uncle Ivan would be stopping in three times a week to check in with me. I did see Biz Bag Betsy but never saw Uncle Ivan.

And just like that I was the man of the house.

Looking back on it, this all was what was needed for my parents, and deep down she knew my dad was right, they had done all that they could for her family, she needed to hear it from him. She felt guilty for putting him through so much, and her small tryst with Detective Underwood over the course of the spring wasn't something she was proud of.

With Club Leman out of the picture, my crew now minus Kenny focused our time on small house parties over the summer.

The biggest event we had was a block party.

I went before the town board, and petitioned them to close off our road for twelve hours, on 10 August, 1980. I called it, "The Genie Productions Cultural Fest."

Lucinda's host family owned a plant nursery and had them dress up our back yard with colorful blooming plants. I latched on to the idea and had a company fix up the entire back yard with new furniture and an outdoor bar with colorful umbrellas. We did this because people were bound to spill over into our yard from the block party, and they did.

This was the very first time I was with my entire crew, but did nothing but sit back with Lucinda and enjoyed the music as a spectator. Enjoying Wheels mix the albums, and Coon Skin singing. It was free admission and we estimated there to have been one thousand people there from the north and south sides, as well as from the Devil's Lake areas.

We had tribal members set up tents for fry bread, dance events, and of course Ed Longbow with his mobile bar tent. Bear Claws Bakery was there, and sold pastries and fresh bread.

By this time we all had developed our individual music mixing styles. I was more conservative with my selections, and had no real skill except for my ear for the music, and what had worked in the past. Mule Train was semi conservative but played cuts of music that I had never thought of together. Trying to explain how Meals on Wheels fit into this scheme is difficult, but may be best explained that he didn't seem to follow any conservatism at all in his music selections. He was strictly freestyle and mashed up samples of Rock, Jazz, Country and Rhythm and Blues into a cacophony of abstract amazement. Music that would normally and under the best conditions never fit together, he made fit together. Perhaps fit is the wrong word? He made it flow together, and the thing of it was no one ever stopped dancing though he mixed over a hundred times in 45 minutes. Young and old alike, many of those that were not even dancers would find themselves swaying to his music. I witnessed this at the cultural fest, when the senior citizens that owned the Bear Claw Bakery heard Meals on Wheels' music and they were drawn out to the middle of the street dancing the Lindy Hop. I saw other old timers dancing the Rumba to his music. In fact, that same day Ms. Sadie Waskins was there in her wheelchair expressing her dance by rolling back and forth and shaking her head to the music while wearing her old blue house dress.

But by far the craziest thing or maybe to some the most refreshing thing was witnessing Peter Dean Vanarski and his wife Dottie May appear at the Cultural festival that day. They hung out at the Feathers beverage tent drinking Vodka. When they heard a particular sample that "Wheels" played, they made a dash to the middle of the street to dance. I stood and watched them both join hands and do some sort of Clogging combined with The Texas Two-step dance. All the while Peter Dean squinted and Dottie May sucked on her cigarette. It was a spectacle for both men and women to see. The men were all strangely fascinated by Dottie May's lewd crotch hugging black stretch pants, meanwhile the women that watched were outraged and repulsed. One lady from Devil's Lake, and I remember this very clearly, stood with her six year old son watching the Vanarski's dance. She and her son stood watching Dottie May for a few seconds when suddenly she covered the boy's eyes with her hand and shuffled him away from the area.

Mule Train literally rolled on the ground laughing at them, and pointing at Coon Skin and then his parents. Coon Skin oozed with embarrassment at all of this, and for once had nothing to say.

It was a real event, we gave away bottles of the fancy booze we had collected, promotional record albums, had dance contests, and a grab bag event.

The music then was no longer Disco, but "Hip Hop."

Each weekend after that, from late August until September we rented the church hall, and continued our "Throw Downs." These were busy times with Genie Productions, and the church hall would fill up within 30 minutes of opening the doors.

Meals on Wheels continued to take parts of songs and mix them with other parts, in short or long loop. This idea was incredibly successful, and became what we were known for in those days. There were party-goers, and even club-goers from Leman that began to follow us, and came to any event in which we played.

I took over Kenny's job of hooking up the sound system wires, and soldering components, patch cords, and tuning the mixer. While I did so, I would quietly speak out loud to Kenny about what I was doing, who of course wasn't there but in jail. While under the table with a flashlight in my mouth, keeping both hands free connecting cables from the mixer to the equalizers, from the equalizers to the noise and feedback limiters, then from there the litany of cables interfacing to the amplifiers, before extending out to the speakers. I would pretend Kenny was there beside me, and helping me. I was missing him very badly. There was a hole in my heart without him.

Once I got the system working I let Wheels do all the mixing, and rapping, taking turns with Mule Train.

I sat with Lucinda at the door, or with Ed at the bar.

201

Ed saw the pain in my heart and we spoke a great deal about it, while we sipped a beer or two together while we tended bar.

Things were never the same without Kenny.

In the meantime, I wrote to Kenny, and I remember Lucinda and I going to visit him once or twice in the county jail. We found him agitated, erratic and loopy without a grasping concept of what was actually happening to him.

With my mother and father away, I settled into a new routine of cooking for myself, washing my own clothes, and school shopping. Of course, Lucinda was there to help, and I kept a house full of my crew almost every night of the week.

Every few days I'd have adult visitors.

Betsy would come in every so often with food she had prepared, and would fill the fridge up with milk and juices for me. I always wanted to ask her about the weed she kept, but I never did. I could see suspicion in her eyes when she came to the house. She always thought I was up to no good, and involved in something. I'm not sure why, it was just her nature.

Detective Underwood came by once a week, to ask about my mother. I just told him she was with my dad. Nevertheless, we would sit and talk for 30-40 minutes before leaving. He was kind, and always well dressed. He didn't speak much about himself. He asked me questions about what I was doing for the summer, and what I'd do with my future. He always handed me his card, and told me to call him day or night if I ever needed him for anything.

Leo Strassenburg stopped in one afternoon, to check on me at the behest of my parents. He wore his beach clothes, which consisted of a black rubber wetsuit, that was unzipped and hung over his waist. I didn't recognize him at first without his hair, but he had a big brown paper bag full of fresh bread from the bakery.

We spoke for three minutes before he set the paper bag and his bill on our kitchen table. He was in a rush and didn't have much time, he seemed always in a hurry.

The next morning an hour before dawn I was awakened by noise in the kitchen. I was happy to hear it because I thought it was my parents returning home, or Lucinda was up making our coffee. But when I felt, she was lying beside me fast asleep.

I was shocked to find Ed Longbow standing in our kitchen, and his father Mr. Elijah Jerimiah Longbow sitting at the table. They both were dressed all in dark green and black hunting clothes.

Mr. Longbow stood and asked my forgiveness for he and Ed waking me, and letting themselves in but he urgently needed to speak with me.

I was very nervous, mainly because my mom had told me how crazy Mr. Longbow was, and it was all very odd to find them in our house.

I had never spoken with Mr. Longbow prior to this or sat and spoken with him.

Up close his features were very pronounced, his eyes were piercingly brown, his gray hair hung down in a thick braided ponytail, I could see some streaks of black and blonde mixed together. A prominent two-inch scar from below his left eye zipped across his cheek. And his neck was bulging and pulsing. Mr. EJ had all of his teeth, and a gold cap near the side that glistened as he spoke.

He spoke in low tones that possessed incredible authority.

Mr. E.J. Longbow's dark eyes locked onto my very soul like a predator with an ice cold ferocity and an unwavering stern expression, so much so that the hair came up on the back of my neck. All of my muscles shook and were ready to explode in flight! I was forced to look away in order to cope with his gaze. Ed was also very intense that morning, and in the way I had only seen him act when we were in school together.

On the other hand Mr. E. J. Longbow spoke in a beautiful and almost musical Algonquin in very short sentences.

"I'm sorry to meet you like this, do you understand?"

I simply nodded my head yes, and tried to not say anything more.

"I need to know who it was that contacted you from the Russo group?"

I told Mr. Longbow the best way I knew how, that it was Detective Underwood.

When I said that name he merely blinked a few times, and nodded his head.

He asked me to tell him all the exact details.

With this question, I had to switch to English a few times, but nervously told him about the meeting at the skating rink, who was there, and what they asked me.

He asked me to think carefully if they said anything about the Tribal School, and or the casino. I told him that Mr. Russo had mentioned the word "War."

Once I said that he nodded his head, thanked me and he and Ed looked at each other briefly.

Unlike most other adults, Mr. EJ was honest, and he didn't ask questions to which he already knew the answer. He spoke truth, it was firm and to the point.

He complimented my language use and demanded that I never say anything about our meeting. After which he smiled, then asked me in a polite manner to make this meeting private, saying, "it would be better to not remember I had ever been here." Ed stood nodding his head in concurrence. I was placed in a trance by them, and instantly forgot anything and everything I said.

He got up and left not saying another word; it was only then that I saw two men in dark clothes in our back yard move swiftly into the woods behind our house.

When I walked them out, one of the men in dark hunting clothes approached me and spoke to me in perfect Algonquin and handed me an envelope. I took it and thanked him; though I did not initially recognize him I did recognize the voice. It was Terry Lunette from Club Leman.

The note said, "sorry this was late getting to you. Thank you for all the help." Five one hundred dollar bills for our final night at the club, the night it was raided and closed.

From a Mitaaswi Animosh confidential informant, Mr. E. J. Longbow knew that the entire crew, Sandy Salucci, his legal assistant, the big man in the blue suit, Detective Underwood and Alberticio Russo would be at the skating rink that morning. He wanted to confirm what they had said to me if anything. It was odd since I had never told Ed or anyone of the meeting I had with them that day. I can only assume I was being followed or someone observed me going in or coming from the upstairs offices of the Skating Rink. That morning. I told Mr. E. J. Longbow the truth of the racist coach, the Detective, the stolen amplifier, Russo and a man named Sandy at the meeting.

Ninety minutes after the kitchen meeting, Club Zanzibar and the skating rink were fire bombed, and razed to the ground. Mr. Alberticio Russo and four of his business associates were said to have been in one of the buildings at the time, but no bodies were ever discovered.

Sandy Salucci, his legal assistant, the big man in the blue suit and Detective Underwood had been at the meeting, but left earlier than expected due to them all taking an earlier flight to Pittsburgh.

The summer flew by very quickly, and two days before I began my senior year in Riverside High School, my parents returned.

They were like brand new parents, speaking softly with each other, and I saw my dad pull out my mom's chair for her to sit down. It was like they were newlyweds.

They told me, once I graduated they were selling the house, and moving to New Mexico for good.

Being a senior in high school was completely different than I expected.

I had only one class in the morning, and one class right after lunch. I no longer saw Lucinda in school, and only saw Ed Longbow in my afternoon class. Which was good since we would meet at the local deli and have lunch, maybe even drink a beer or two before our class together.

I remember this day in October very clearly. Ed Longbow, and Lucinda and I sat at the pizza parlor sharing a pizza and a pitcher of Molson's beer. We were planning a Halloween party throw down, in the event center of the Hilton Hotel in New Port. It was at this very time, we learned that Kenny had hung himself in the county jail. It was Betsy who seemed to know just where to find me to deliver this news.

We sat for a few moments staring at Betsy, who offered no other information , in fact after delivering the news to us she excused herself to get back to her TV soap operas that were about the start. We all stared at each other while Lucinda began to cry and hugged me. I was in shock hearing this, and didn't cry but felt pain in my stomach and neck, like my soul was being torn out. Ed looked incredibly sad as well, and put his head on the table, after finishing his beer.

At first it was complete disbelief, and I had never seen Biz Bag Betsy as reliable. Sadly, this was true.

DARK DAYS OF GRIEF

I had never seen my father cry, or become teary eyed. Even at Ralph Waskins funeral he stood strong and resolute while the rest of us cried. However, when I got home that day he sat at the kitchen table with his handkerchief, eyes bloodshot and his nose running over the news of Kenny's death. My mother wasn't in such good shape. She had taken some anxiety medicine that the doctor had prescribed and was planning to go to bed as soon as I got home. When I arrived they both hugged me and we all stood hugging and crying over this horrible news.

I guess as a kid, perhaps I never could conceive what a permanent thing death is, and while I was extremely sad, the gravity of what had happened was beyond my understanding. Believe it or not I only knew how terrible and awful a thing had occurred because I didn't have to go to school the rest of the week or the week after that. My mother had spoken to Lucinda and asked her to get my work from my classes and to bring it home for me.

Riverside's high school principal and guidance counselor called the house to express their condolences. They also reminded my mother that in order to miss so much school and not risk being held back a grade I would need a doctor's note.

My parents called Dr. McMasters and off I went to see her again, but this time for grief counseling.

My mom and dad and I arrived to the office of Dr. McMasters at 0845 for my 0900 appointment, and she swept us all in this time. We all sat and looked around, while I watched my dad's eyes looking at the back of her head and all of the civic citations and diplomas on the walls in their matching dusty pine frames. His eyes then were drawn to the coffee table in front of us covered in books written by Dr. McMasters. The one book he picked up was one that I had not noticed the last time I was there.

It was an old man sitting at a piano with a young boy sitting on his lap. Entitled "Grandpa Plays Old Dick Like the Best of Them."

My dad knew I had been there before, and he knew of this woman but had never met her previously.

When she turned around in her chair she looked right at my dad and said, "So, how long have you been on the booze and pills?"

Stunned, my dad politely told her that we were here for grief counselling over the death of his young nephew.

She turned around, grabbed another stack of papers, and said, "Oh, I see Judge Smith sent you here for vagrancy and destruction of public property."

That was when my father's face went blank, his eyes squinted with disgust and after standing up, he grabbed our hands and we quickly walked out of there. Dr McMasters yelled, "Leaving only goes badly against your case!"

"That was interesting," my father said as we drove away with my mom giggling.

In addition, my father stayed home, and my mother never left his side, or my side. She cooked spaghetti and made a meatloaf, cleaned and catered to my needs.

Two days later my parents and I all went to buy a black suit for me. In all my years I had never gone shopping for anything with my father. They wouldn't allow me to leave their sight during this time and my father even came into the fitting room with me.

That afternoon at Albert's funeral home was when we all went to see Kenny's body for the first time since I had seen him in jail a month earlier.

The casket was open and Kenny lay there and he looked like a handsome mannequin. I stood studying his face and his unusual red lips while warm tears came down my face. My parents stood behind me, hugging me and we all were crying by now, except my father, who now had come to grips with what had become of his nephew.

We sat in the first rows of the funeral chapel. It was then that I saw the Bootleg Brothers come in and walk over to the casket and view his body. Then came Ed Longbow, and Lucinda. They politely offered their condolences to my mother and father. After a while I got up and went outside with Ed Longbow and the Bootleg Brothers while Lucinda and I held hands.

There stood Mule Train in his blue sweat suit and he had a brindle Great Dane on a leash that he had just found named "Tiny." We all were happy to see him, and he said he had walked there since he couldn't get his car to start.

Coon Skin pulled up in his Cadillac with Wendy and Meals on Wheels.

We all mustered and hung out outside the funeral chapel that afternoon and had a good time just being there all of us together one last time. We spent time together.

It was not long after this that some of the students from Riverside high school showed up. Others that saw the small crowd and recognizing Coon Skin's car stopped and it turned into a small party outside in the parking lot of the chapel. Coon Skin opened the trunk of his Caddy and put a cassette tape in from the cultural fest and turned up the volume.

Ed had a few bottles in his Beverage van, and we passed around cups of wine and booze while we stood around remembering my beautiful cousin. Some stories made us laugh, and others had some of us crying all over again, but in a cathartic way.

I must say it made me feel warm inside to have this get together of my crew and fellow students during such a difficult time.

At 7 p.m. once the service was over my parents both
emerged from the chapel, and were surprised to see so many
young people that had turned out to support our family and
show love for Kenny's life, as short as it was. My mother and
father finally got in the car, and headed home with Lucinda and
Mule Train and me, with his Great Dane, Tiny, in the back seat.

My father stopped at Ralph and Sadie Waskins' house and
dropped off Mule Train and Tiny the Great Dane.

Once we got home, Lucinda and I sat up watching television while my parents went into the bedroom to rest.

My parents and especially my mother were in the worst
shape of all from this, because what they didn't share with me
was that my uncle the Right Reverend IC Guise was missing
and try as they may, he couldn't be found. This meant that again
my father was on the hook, this time to pay the bill for this entire tragic event. The enormous bill of the funeral was perhaps
sadder than the death itself, at least that's what was on his mind
at the time. He also reassured my mother that he had run off
somewhere and he would show up sooner or later. He explained
to my mother again about her brother being a grasshopper and
that "We were the Ants."

The next morning my parents, Lucinda and I went to
the Pill Hill Parsonage and began to clean up since they had
planned the repass there once the funeral was completed. We
had expected to be gone most of the day, however we returned
very quickly.

Once we arrived to Pill Hill and its beautiful architecture
, fresh air and trimmed ornate lawns, my father felt good and
thought the air was refreshing. My father and I got some trash
bags, while Lucinda and my mom attempted to get to the kitch-
en. My father made his way to the third floor then back to the
ground floor and we all clearly heard him say

"ShiiiiiiiiiiT, There is No Fucking Way!!"

He walked right back out, and stood beside the car smoking his cigar.

He said that he would rather rent St Patrick's Cathedral before he would clean up that mess. I don't think he liked roaches, while he tried to explain to my mother that they could infest our house if they stayed in there too long. My mom relented and we decided to leave without cleaning up, however my father made us take off our shoes and socks and inspected us thoroughly before he allowed us to get in the car. I'm glad he did since Lucinda had what my father called a pregnant roach in her hair.

On the way home he explained to us that my uncle had a real mental problem that caused him to live like that, and it was filthy and he had no idea that his life was so foul.

Two weeks went by very slowly while my grieving time merged into fall break. During this time my parents sought to find and wait for the return of IC Guise and felt that best instead of just promptly burying Kenny.

Lucinda, Ed Longbow and I went walking through Freemont Cemetery, which had three parts all connected by an improved surface road.

We left the Genie Love Van on the first part, and walked slowly over the gravel road speaking quietly about the latest song that was released by Joan Jett. We didn't like the song, but it had a nice usable drum break Wheels could use.

When we got to the third section of the driveway, it was the section from which we could see the ballpark, and the southeastern side of Riverside High School.

I saw the path where Kenny and I had parked that wonderful night so long ago when I lost my virginity to Summer. I looked at it and saw some bottle caps, and a few beer cans in the bushes. But what struck me most was a cedar tree. I don't know if it was a white or red cedar but it was an old, tall cedar tree with a thick low hanging branch. This branch was scuffed up slightly from kids playing upon it.

I explained some of the details of the tree with Lucinda and Ed, and we agreed that we should ask if this is where Kenny could be buried.

We went right home, and asked my mother if she'd call Albert's and see if we could buy a plot under the cedar tree.

My parents had used $10,000 of the money we had made at the club to pay for his funeral, and they felt that paying a bit extra for this plot wasn't a problem at all.

THE COUNTY JAIL

When the arrest sweep happened and Kenny was taken into custody he was alarmed but not overly so. He didn't resist the arrest or even object to the officers that night.

He was put in the men's jail in New Port County and in general population, along with thirty others from that night. They all were still high from the night of drinking and using copious amounts of the white stimulant powder. It was a group setting and most if not all were in party spirits with numb heads and loose bodies.

That night and over the following days, one by one each member of the sweep as it was called, were bailed out and happily left.

Kenny waited patiently for my parents, his dad, or even Sandy Salucci to come bail him out.

What he didn't know was that this "sweep" was focused mainly upon him. The weight he was holding was considerable at 2.6 kilos or 5 pounds of very cut down powder. In fact, the powder he had that night had barely registered as cocaine, since it had been watered down 90% with Mannitol and baby laxa-

213

tive. But it was still a federal offense, that drew federal charges and the full weight of the war on drugs was laying upon my cousin's beautiful shoulders.

Mr. Strassenberg did pay him a visit and told him of my parents' desire of getting him out, and that he'd be in touch, however that was now over a month ago.

His high had long since disappeared and the pangs of withdrawal had poignantly seized him. It disrupted his thinking, his sleep and every nerve of his body.

He wrote letters to the judge, my mom and dad, his dad, and his mother. But mailed them all to me that I should forward them. I read them, and so did Lucinda. They were filled with contrition saying that he wanted to get out of jail and lead a full life. He even had promised to go back to school. They were beautiful letters, from a beautiful soul, my big brother.

His father, the Reverend Ivan Conrad Guise had come to see him, and make inroads upon freeing his son. He too was surprised at the amount of bail and the charges of trafficking.

Desperate to help his son, Ivan Guise decided to pay a visit to the local bank downtown. He met with the chief loan officer of Riverside Savings and Loan and politely asked for a loan in the amount of one million dollars.

When asked about collateral, the Reverend promptly reached into the breast pocket of his long black cassock, and produced a deed to three acres of beachfront land in swanky Horse Neck.

The loan officer was quite surprised to see such a valuable document, and it all seemed in order with all the official stamps, seals and paid property tax receipts. He recorded the location, and helped my uncle complete and sign the loan request document. He made a copy of the deed, and handed the original back to the Reverend.

"The next step in the loan process will be an appraisal of the land, and from there we can speak more on how much of a loan we can lend based on the value of the land," said the loan officer.

Less than twenty-four hours later a land appraiser and survey crew upon the behest of the bank arrived at the location accurately spelled out on the deed and loan application.

They went right to work measuring, recording distances and placing flags on the land and near the high and low tide marks. The land appraiser was thrilled to report that in his opinion the land was worth a staggering four million dollars.

The loan officer called the Reverend Ivan C. Guise with the great news. That news was that the bank will offer him a loan in the amount of eighty percent of four million dollars, and explained some of the routine terms of the loan process. The loan officer was augustly giddy to have such a valuable customer on the phone and made light talk about the weather, and of his family.

Later that day a tribal police officer that was on a routine beach patrol noticed the survey flags, and stopped to investigate. He reported the flags and their location to his shift supervisor, who passed it on to his supervisor. At first it was thought that children had been on the beach playing, or that a tribal fisherman had marked the beach for night surf fishing.

The name on a flag revealed it was from an out of state land appraiser that had unknowingly trespassed on tribal land, or had gotten incorrect coordinates. It was quickly discovered that Riverside Savings and Loan had ordered the survey, based upon an official deed of land ownership and a signed loan application. The head of tribal law enforcement immediately turned the entire matter over to the "Mitaaswi Animosh" for remedy.

The Reverend was notified by the loan officer that his loan was tentatively approved and the bank just needed a day to prepare the paperwork and the transaction would be closed via their local attorney's office.

My uncle's document skills were superlative, because even the bank's attorney saw it as legitimate, and the land had indeed been transferred to him in 1956.

The night of October 2nd just after midnight, six dark figures moved toward the church parsonage. The men, dressed in black on black paramilitary fatigues, heads covered with black nylon balaclava and wearing black NATO issued military boots, entered through the back door and three made entrance through the front door of the Hudson Street Parsonage.

They were armed to the teeth with large bore pistols, long barrel military rifles with suppressors, concussive hand grenades, smoke grenades, tear gas canisters, and incendiary grenades all hung securely from their black nylon web suspenders.

One man stood watch at the front door, and one man stood at the back door, while the others entered the once palatial parsonage.

As quiet and stealthy as ghosts, the four made their way over fusty pizza boxes, passed rank, overflowing litter boxes, and up the steps to the second floor bedroom. Not one dog barked, not one cat even hissed or meowed as they skillfully crept over mountains of full plastic garbage bags.

The two "Mitaaswi Animosh" at both doors had large roaches climbing quickly up their thighs. They held the doors open while dogs and cats ran past them into the fresh night air; nonplussed, they continued their mission. The two at the door were in radio communication with the two in the awaiting van parked around the corner.

Secretly providing over watch at 10,000 feet above was a black on black Bell 205 Iroquois helicopter with two of the "Mitaaswi Animosh" piloting. They were in constant radio communication with the two in the van, the two at the doors, and the four now upstairs in the parsonage.

The Reverend was awakened by a bright flashlight in his face, and before he could scream a rag soaked with ether based starter fluid was smashed into and held over his face.

His limp body was rolled into a black body bag, and was quickly carried downstairs and placed in the back of a panel van, and swept away. The helo stayed in sustained over watch before returning to God's Breath.

It was only around the time of our Cultural Fest that the reality of it all began coming down on Kenny. He did meet with a court appointed lawyer who told him he was looking at twenty years, and out in ten since this was his first offense, but went on to suggest that he cooperate with the government. In cooperating he'd be required to do what I did with the Henry Martinez case, only disclose where he got the powder from, and if he knew where they got it. They wanted names, which was the only card Kenny had left to play.

In the meantime, and what very few knew was that Santo Sandy Salucci was behind the entire bust at Club Lemans. His inner circle of course knew of it as well as saintly and well-dressed Detective Underwood. Since it directly affected the Pasqotouk Nation, the Mitaaswi Animosh knew of all the working parts of Santo's machinations to shut down one of their enterprises.

They placed the bait, and now just waited for the results, which meant Club Zanzibar would be back in full swing with Leman permanently closed, this was before the fire bombing and apparent kidnapping of Alberticio Russo and associates.

With the Captain in his pocket he would be able to move major weight of different powders like heroin, and cocaine and get a heads up of any of those pesky drug busts. The loose ends need only be snipped, and his bottom line would be restored.

My dear and beautiful cousin was simply now one of the loose ends.

Months before the big Lemans bust, Coach Don Marietti was arrested and charged with the brutal murder and grizzly mutilation of Henry Martinez, and his brother Alex. Coach Don Marietti was one of Kenny's only familiar faces left in the jail at the time.

He and the coach had a long history. Coach was now his only friend and now his medicine man.

Coach Don Marietti had a mainline supply of cocaine, marijuana and heroin into the jail.

There is always shock and staunch disbelief that drugs exist in jail or prison. This is one of the best places to have a drug concession, since there is no competition, and the prices are almost tripled from street prices. Also those that sneak it in are already inmates or those convicted of crimes. It also finds its way into the jails through those that operate the jail, since the amount of money is such a powerful temptation.

Sandy had this all planned, and the final job before Coach Don would be out on lack of evidence was to cut the loose end.

BLESSED ASSURANCE

The morning of October 3rd was a busy morning at Feathers Beverages and Liquors due to two semis that had come at the exact same time to deliver wine and beer from the supplier in Colorado.

Both registers were very busy since a busload of 50 hikers had arrived and were to be heading out later that afternoon to the Pasqotouk wilderness adventure that the tribe had every October. Additionally, the town of Horse Neck was ramping up for their annual Octoberfest. They were expecting many thousands of visitors from near and far for this event.

A locked freezer located in the dankest and most distant corner of Feathers Liquors is where the Reverend slowly regained consciousness and his groggy eyes were drawn to a five foot condensing fan that thrummed above him on a dark metal ceiling, and it was only then that he realized he was freezing cold.

Above him the promising sounds of voices, boxes being moved around, and the muffled sound of a forklift whirred and hummed. Sounds of large clanking of metal doors being closed shut, were very discernable just behind him. The smell of the ether starting fluid had burned his sinuses but discernable was the smell of stale beer and wine with wet boxes that entered his nose.

On the other side of a wall he heard the muffled churning of a diesel engine that sat idling at the loading dock.

His eyes were drawn to a small shiny object on the smelly and dank cold concrete floor in front of him. The Reverend squinted a bit before realizing it was a 2 inch solid gold Italian horn and a clasped thick 22 inch gold Figaro chain.

He wanted to reach out and grab it, but as much as he tried his arms would not respond. They were numb and lifeless.

His arms and legs were tightly bound with red 550 paracord and he lay atop of a wooden loading palette right next to a five foot tall stack of beer and liquor boxes, deep within the basement of Feather's Beverage and Liquor.

A three-foot long piece of tan packing tape was wrapped tightly around his head and over his mouth.

Mr. E. J. Longbow's face slowly appeared from his periphery and told him plainly, "I will remove this tape if you promise to keep quiet."

The Reverend nodded his head.

Mr. E. J. produced a shiny box cutter blade, and made two slices on either side of The Reverend's mouth cutting his cold skin before he sadistically tore the strong adhesive from his mouth slowly while warm blood ran down both sides of his chin. The Reverend's face was so cold, he couldn't feel that he had been cut nor could he feel the blood that ran down his face.

"There, isn't that better?" Mr. EJ asked then patted the Reverend's head like a well behaving dog, while he slid the blade back in his hip pocket after wiping the blood from it on the Reverend's vile urine stained night shirt.

The Reverend could breathe much better now, and was becoming more lucid.

"I have only two questions for you, Reverend," said Longbow softly.

"Do you understand?" he whispered.

The Reverend now crying nodded his head yes.

"Where did you get the deed for our land?"

Unable to fashion a lie, the Reverend answered truthfully. "I made it twenty years ago, on my printing press."

"Who helped you?" Mr. EJ grunted.

"No one helped me, I did it myself."

Mr. Longbow nodded his head and uttered "uh huh" before whispering: "Thank you, you now are free to go and warm up," Mr. EJ said reassuringly

My uncle sighed with great relief, and twisted his tightly bound wrists knowing that they would soon be free. He didn't know where he was, or what had happened, but he needed to get out of wherever this was to warm up. He recognized Mr. E. J. Longbow, but from hypothermia he couldn't remember how or from where. But he thought, *as soon as I warm up I will explain about my son needing bail money and this all was just a misunderstanding.* The Reverend began humming, "Just a Closer Walk With Thee."

Quickly, and after that brief exchange and true to his word in releasing The Reverend, Mr. E.J Longbow placed a thick empty champagne box over the Reverend's head. He removed a chrome snub nose .38 revolver from his waistband, and at close range fired two rounds into the box.

Gunsmoke smoldered from the box's open seams, and it filled with my uncle's bright red blood. Not one warm drop spattered from the velocity of the two slugs.

Mr. Longbow shoved the warm revolver back into his waistband and calmly walked back to his loading dock and continued checking in kegs of beer.

On October 3rd somewhere in-between the second and third shift at the county jail, Coach Don Marietti presented Kenny with a familiar small wax bag.

He offered it as a gift and was a sample of "Good Shit directly from South America," from which he wanted Kenny's opinion.

After handing the small bag to Kenny, Coach Marietti began to rant about his days playing professional hockey. He reminisced about all the cities he had played in listing them by name, Toronto, Minneapolis, Detroit and the women he had met there. His prowess with women, "especially the bitches on the road." What a powerful forward he was as a professional and of all the money he made, and had stashed some of it away. He went on to graphically speak of his wife, and girlfriends, and what he planned to do with them when he got home. He mentioned Sandy Salucci and spoke a great deal of Club Zanzibar and the skating rink, and how everyone there liked him. He went on about how important he was there. How the coaching job was awful working with the black niggers and the red niggers and how he didn't care for them. He pointed out how different Kenny was from the normal niggers there. He spoke to him about what he knew of his mother and more of his private personal history. Kenny didn't reply to this but he continued speaking while Kenny carefully dumped the contents of the bag on a small table and used the edge of the wax bag to make straight lines of the powder.

This Good Shit, was a mixture of cocaine, strong barbiturate, ketamine horse tranquilizer and uncut heroin mixed together in a fine white confectionary powder.

Kenny gladly snorted it all once the coach politely declined to join in.

It burned his mucous membranes terribly, so much so that his nose bled after the first snort.

This powerful and deadly concoction put my cousin into a narcotic "Head High" stupor, with the slowing of his respiration, and heart rate. His stupor felt better than anything he had ever experienced, with warming of his extremities and kaleidoscopic images of Lake Michigan and of his mother urging him on to swim in the warm waters toward her. Hallucinating images continued in these seconds of his old granny being kind, and of his new Adidas shoes, and how warm and soft they felt on his feet.

"Swim, Kenny!" Helen said smiling and cheering him on-ward! "Swim, my beautiful son!" He swam smiling with the love in his heart of a supportive, wonderful, beautiful mother!

"Mom!" he shouted, arriving in her arms.

Coach Don stood behind Kenny and quickly wrapped a grimy wet bed sheet completely around his neck. He began powerfully twisting and wringing it with his brawny and blue veined hands. He then hoisted its bitter end over a drainpipe and skillfully tied a knot near his powerless hands.

Coach Don Marietti, quietly returned to his bunk and fell into a deep sleep.

Thank you for reading " The Age of Guise" give us a like or review on Facebook. In the meanwhile , keep an eye out for the sequel, "The Rise of Longbow" on Amazon December 2022

The Rise of Longbow

Longshore workers arduously and precisely operated massive gantry cranes lifting tonnage filled metal containers out of the hold of container ship "Mildred Madina".

Lines of bright red and dark green diesel big rigs, sat at idle awaiting their loads at the busy Pittsburgh ship yards.

Once loaded and only after clearing US Customs they would be allowed to leave.

A five man team of United States Border agents and their dogs walked the length of the mighty "Mildred Madina" searching and waiting for an alert from their obedient canines.

The Captain and First Mate made random inspections of the large boxes, in a show of compliance witnessed by one of the Border agent teams. While they did this a careful examination of the bill of lading and inspection of the truck sized container was carried out. This was to insure what was on the bill matched what was inside to the letter.

After many hours all was found to be in order, and Captain Detorres returned to his plush and warm state room.

58 year old Captain Detorres felt good and was in cheerful spirits mostly due to how much extra money he was being paid for this trip, not to mention the sweet plans he had to visit a young Spanish woman he knew in Pittsburgh.

His crew had long since gone ashore, and port security kept the boats gangway secure. Captain Detorres had just completed changing into his smart white and blue dress uniform in his state room, and had just shaved, showered, and laced up his shiny black patent leather dress shoes.

It was at this very moment, when Captain Detorres was startled when he heard a man's voice from just behind him. The voice was throaty and deep, while the hair on the very back of the captain's neck stood on edge. At first it was a throat clearing, then a snorted but very discernable word entered his large hairy ears .

"Where?"

Startled and surprised the captain quickly turned around and to his horror three large and powerfully built soldiers stood shoulder to shoulder in front of him.

Mr. Elijah J Longbow in the center and two others that stood powerfully on either side of him.

"Nish" and "Major Jung" at his flanks wearing black balaclava over their heads and neck. They wore loose fitting black on black rip stock NATO uniforms , and black nylon combat boots.

Mr. Longbow stood powerfully akimbo , his .38 caliber stainless pistol securely wedged in his waist band and tightly against his flat stomach. His 10 gauge Browning shotgun slung over his back like that of a Japanese katana sword.

The other two men had their pistols holstered, and their M16 rifles slung. "Nish" held a cattle prod and "Major Jung" bounced and loudly slapped a leather covered heavily weighted blackjack off the palm of his left hand, impatiently.

Captain Detorres yelled and called the men trespassers and stowaways on his ship! Without getting an answer or even a response, he yelled again in fear.

"There is no money here!"

Still the men stood silently.

In desperation he yelled in Spanish, and then yelled in Kurdish, but now calling them Pirates !!

No matter what he said there was no reply, nor did the men move an inch other than the slapping of the lead filled leather wrapped blackjack.

Mr. Elijah Jeremiah Longbow remained akimbo along with the two members of the Mitaaswi Animosh blocking the captain's escape.

"Last time Captain, Where?" asked Mr. Ej Longbow.

"Where What?" answered the captain.

Once he said this Mr. Longbow charged him like a brahma bull and powerfully grabbed the Captain by the lapels. This grab was so powerful that the captain's head snapped back, and stunned him. He quickly spun the captain around holding his weight and wrapped his massive arm around his neck. This caused the captain to cry out loudly, "HELP ME! Help Me!"

Mr. Elijah Longbow now whispered in his ear calmly and quietly, "shush"

This was the exact time that "Nish" stepped forward and poked the captain's solar plexus with the cattle prod. The sound of a loud snapping spark, and the smell of burning cotton and flesh filled the plush state room.

Slowly the captain awoke tied to the commode in his state room as naked as the day he was born!

He was tied face up with his arms bound to his legs. His left wrist was tightly tied to his right ankle, and his right wrist was securely tied to his left ankle with black 550 para cord across the base of the fancy and private ceramic toilet. His back was painfully hyper extended and arched backward over the commode

"Major Jung", now spoke to the groggy captain.

"THE DOPE !! Where is the container with the dope ?"